Modern Developments
in the Mechanics of Continua

Contributors to This Volume

Th. Alziary de Roquefort

D. R. Axelrad

Jose Barberan F.

Vaughn C. Behn

Bernard D. Coleman

Subhendu K. Datta

A. G. Fabula

R. L. Fosdick

R. Goethals

Morton E. Gurtin

Ismael Herrera R.

W. Jaunzemis

J. L. Lumley

E. W. Merrill

H. S. Mickley

A. J. A. Morgan

A. C. Pipkin

F. W. Smith

K. A. Smith

Gerald A. Strobel

W. D. Taylor

George B. Thurston

C. Truesdell

P. S. Virk

C.-C. Wang

R. N. Yong

Modern Developments
in the Mechanics of Continua

Proceedings of an International Conference on Rheology
Held at the Pinebrook Conference Center of
Syracuse University
Pinebrook, New York, August 23–27, 1965

Supported by The New York State Science and Technology Foundation

Edited by SALAMON ESKINAZI

**Department of Mechanical and Aerospace Engineering
Syracuse University
Syracuse, New York**

ACADEMIC PRESS   New York · London 1966

ACADEMIC PRESS INC.
111 Fifth Avenue, New York, New York 10003

United Kingdom Edition published by
ACADEMIC PRESS INC. (LONDON) LTD.
Berkeley Square House, London W.1

LIBRARY OF CONGRESS CATALOG CARD NUMBER: 66-29430

PRINTED IN THE UNITED STATES OF AMERICA

List of Contributors

Numbers in parentheses indicate the pages on which the authors' contributions begin.

Th. Alziary de Roquefort, E.N.S.M.A., University of Poitiers, Poitiers, France (139)

D. R. Axelrad, Department of Mechanical Engineering, McGill University, Montreal, Canada (183)

Jose Barberan F., Instituto de Geofísica, Universidad Nacional de México, Mexico City, Mexico (175)

Vaughn C. Behn, School of Civil Engineering, Cornell University, Ithaca, New York (193)

Bernard D. Coleman, Mellon Institute, Pittsburgh, Pennsylvania (165)

Subhendu K. Datta,† Department of Aerospace Engineering Sciences, University of Colorado, Boulder, Colorado (73)

A. G. Fabula,‡ The Pennsylvania State University, University Park, Pennsylvania (145)

R. L. Fosdick, Department of Mechanics, Illinois Institute of Technology, Chicago, Illinois (109)

R. Goethals, E.N.S.M.A., University of Poitiers, Poitiers, France (139)

Morton E. Gurtin, Brown University, Providence, Rhode Island (165)

Ismael Herrera R., Instituto de Geofísica, Universidad Nacional de México, Mexico City, Mexico (175)

W. Jaunzemis, Department of Engineering Mechanics, The Pennsylvania State University, University Park, Pennsylvania (65)

J. L. Lumley, Department of Aeronautical Engineering, The Pennsylvania State University, University Park, Pennsylvania (145)

† *Present address:* Department of Aeronautical Engineering, Indian Institute of ~~Higher~~ Technology, ~~Khairpur~~ Kanpur, India.

‡ *Present address:* United States Naval Ordnance Test Station, Pasadena, California.

v

E. W. Merrill, Department of Chemical Engineering, Massachusetts Institute of Technology, Cambridge, Massachusetts (37)

H. S. Mickley, Department of Chemical Engineering, Massachusetts Institute of Technology, Cambridge, Massachusetts (37)

A. J. A. Morgan, Department of Engineering, University of California, Los Angeles, California (53)

A. C. Pipkin, Division of Applied Mathematics, Brown University, Providence, Rhode Island (89)

F. W. Smith, Division of Mechanical Engineering, National Research Council of Canada, Ottawa, Ontario, Canada (13)

K. A. Smith, Department of Chemical Engineering, Massachusetts Institute of Technology, Cambridge, Massachusetts (37)

Gerald A. Strobel,† School of Civil Engineering, Cornell University, Ithaca, New York (193)

W. D. Taylor, Department of Biophysics, The Pennsylvania State University, University Park, Pennsylvania (145)

George B. Thurston, Physics Department, Oklahoma State University, Stillwater, Oklahoma (19)

C. Truesdell, Department of Mechanics, The Johns Hopkins University, Baltimore, Maryland (1)

P. S. Virk, Department of Chemical Engineering, Massachusetts Institute of Technology, Cambridge, Massachusetts (37)

C.-C. Wang, Department of Mechanics, The Johns Hopkins University, Baltimore, Maryland (129)

R. N. Yong, Department of Civil Engineering and Applied Mechanics and Soil Mechanics, McGill University, Montreal, Canada (183)

---

† *Present address:* Shellfisheries Management Unit, State of New York Conservation Department, Oakdale, Long Island, New York.

Preface

The papers collected in this volume were presented at the Pinebrook Rheology Conference held on August 23–27, 1965 and sponsored by the Department of Mechanical and Aerospace Engineering at Syracuse University.

These papers were presented and were part of a larger effort at promoting national and international interest in mechanics of continua. During the period of August 9 to September 24, 1965, Dr. C. Truesdell, Distinguished Visiting Professor at Syracuse University and Professor in the Department of Mechanics at The Johns Hopkins University, presented a series of lectures in the form of a course in mechanics of continua.

The Pinebrook Conference was held at one of Syracuse University's Adirondacks Conference Centers located on Upper Saranac Lake in Pinebrook, New York.

S. ESKINAZI

December, 1966

Contents

LIST OF CONTRIBUTORS   v
PREFACE   vii

Thermodynamics of Deformation

C. Truesdell

Text   1

An Alternative to the Continuum—the Aggregate as a Geometrical Basis for the Deformation Tensor and for Theories of Liquids

F. W. Smith

1. Introduction   13
2. The General Aggregate   14
3. "Inherent" and "Flow" Deformation of an Aggregate   15
4. Conclusions   16
    References   17

Shear Wave Propagation in Birefringent Viscoelastic Liquids of Low Rigidity and Low Viscosity

George B. Thurston

1. Introduction   19
2. Propagation Equations   21
3. Experimental Apparatus   23
4. Theoretical Model for a Suspension of Rigid Ellipsoidal Particles   27
5. Experimental Measurements   31
6. Conclusion   35
    References   35

The Critical Wall Shear Stress for Reduction of Turbulent Drag in Pipe Flow

P. S. Virk, E. W. Merrill, H. S. Mickley, and K. A. Smith

1. Introduction   38
2. Previous Investigations   38
3. The Onset of Drag Reduction   38

4. The Onset of Drag Reduction Hypothesis   41
5. Experimental Materials and Apparatus   42
6. Data   42
7. Discussion of Results   48
8. Summary   50
   Appendix: Scaling Rules for the Dissipation Wavenumber, k_d 51
   Nomenclature   52
   References   52

Properties of a Class of Constitutive Equations Stated in a Nontrivial Implicit Form

A. J. A. Morgan

1. Introduction   53
2. Formulation   54
3. Reduction to Component Form   55
4. Properties of the Nondiagonal Solutions   58
5. A Special Case   59
6. Characteristic Surfaces for the Medium   61
7. Conclusions   63
   References   63

Cosserat Continua

W. Jaunzemis

1. Introduction   65
2. Cosserat Continua   66
3. Dipolar Media   70
   References   71

Stability of Couette Flow of Second-Order Fluids between Two Coaxial Circular Cylinders

Subhendu K. Datta

1. Introduction   73
2. Equations   75
3. Solution   77
4. Conclusion   78
   References   87

Approximate Constitutive Equations

A. C. Pipkin

1. Introduction   89
2. Wide-Range and Narrow-Range Descriptions   91
3. One-Dimensional Shearing Motions   92

4. Materials with Memory 92
5. Materials with Fading Memory 94
6. Viscoelastic Fluids 94
7. Small Motions 96
8. Short Motions 97
9. Slow Motions 98
10. Orders of Approximation in Slow Motion 100
11. Analytic Continuation 102
12. Small Motions Superposed on Stress-Relaxation at Constant Deformation 103
13. Small Motions Superposed on Steady Shearing Motion 104
14. Some Remarks on Perturbation Methods 105
15. Conclusion 107
    References 107

Remarks on Compatibility

R. L. Fosdick

1. Introduction 109
2. Kinematic Concepts and Notation 110
3. Other Forms of Compatibility 114
4. Deformations with Constant Strain Invariants 117
5. Equilibrium: Elastic, Incompressible, Isotropic Material 125
   References 127

A Representative Theorem for the Constitutive Equation of Simple Material in Motions with Constant Stretch History

C.-C. Wang

Text 129
References 137

The Problem of a Jet against the Ground. Rheological Solution in the Hodograph Plane

R. Goethals and Th. Alziary de Roquefort

Text 139
References 144

Some Interpretations of the Toms Effect

A. G. Fabula, J. L. Lumley, and W. D. Taylor

1. Introduction 146
2. Virk's Hypothesis 150

3. A Molecular Viscoelasticity Hypothesis   152
4. Comparison with Experiment   155
5. A Molecular Entanglement Hypothesis   156
6. A Shear-Layer Modification Hypothesis   159
7. Conclusions   162
   References   162

Acceleration Waves in Nonlinear Materials

Bernard D. Coleman and Morton E. Gurtin

1. Introduction   165
2. Preliminary Definitions   165
3. Waves in Elastic Materials   167
4. Waves in Linearly Viscoelastic Materials   168
5. Waves in Simple Materials with Memory   169
   References   173

The Speed of Propagation of Signals in Viscoelastic Materials

Jose Barberan F. and Ismael Herrera R.

1. Introduction   175
2. Notation   177
3. Statement of the Problem   179
   References   181

On an Isothermal Flow Function for a Heterogeneous Medium

D. R. Axelrad and R. N. Yong

1. Introduction   183
2. Physical Constants and Microstress-Strain Relations   184
3. Formulation of the Flow Function of a Heterogeneous Medium   186
4. Experimental Considerations   188
   References   191

Mass Transfer into Non-Newtonian Fluids

Vaughn C. Behn and Gerald A. Strobel

1. Introduction   193
2. Theory   193
3. Experimental Apparatus   195
4. Experimental Procedure   197
5. Experimental Results   197
6. Discussion   198
7. Summary and Conclusions   200
   References   200

INDEX   201

Thermodynamics of Deformation

C. TRUESDELL

Department of Mechanics
The Johns Hopkins University
Baltimore, Maryland

On an occasion such as this, the speaker is expected to disclose some earth-shaking discovery of his own. Great international conferences are scheduled at decent intervals, nowadays no less than a week apart, so as to allow such discoveries to be made from one to the next. The only way to be snobbish today in circles of science is to refuse to make any more discoveries and instead devote one's time to learning the state of the subject, like an old-fashioned teacher from the days before research had become a racket for hoodwinking the public into allowing professors something approaching one third of a living wage. With the permission of the experts here assembled, I will explain thermodynamics to the best of my ability to understand it. While I shall present some unpublished material, it will be what I have learned from others.

The danger of crossing the mouth of the dismal cavern of thermodynamics is well known. As I wrote once, but was too tactful ever to publish, "Indeed, there are many who claim to understand thermodynamics, but it is best for them by common consent to avoid the topic in conversation with one another, since it leads to consequences such as can be expected from arguments over politics, religion, or the canons of female beauty. Honesty compels me to confess that in several attempts, made over decades, I have never been able to understand the subject, not only in what others have written on it, but also in my own earlier presentations."

While any physicist selected at random understands thermodynamics perfectly and has only contempt or pity for those unfortunate and unphysical persons who express doubt, if we cast the die a second time and draw a second physicist, we can expect to hear a lively clash as the words "reversible," "irreversible," "adiabatic," "isolated," "thermal contact," "reservoir," "cyclic," "quasistatic," "ideal engine," "boiler," "piston," "condenser," and "universe" contribute to the entropy of the acoustic medium. To overcome the difficulties it is best to follow a simple rule for study of the history of science: setting aside what an author says, see what he does.

Since the earliest thermodynamic researches, two kinds of phenomena have been considered. In the former, different equilibria are compared, without regard to the means, if any, of passing from one to the other. In the latter, the process of interconversion of heat and work is described as it proceeds. As is well known, the former, which really ought to be called *thermostatics*, has lent itself to a modest and successful mathematical theory, elaboration of which fills the major parts of most books on the subject, while the latter, which deserves the name *thermodynamics*, has remained mainly verbal and far from complete. We are not to be deceived by the words "quasi-static process" or "reversible process," for these are mere names for parametric families of equilibria—if we prefer, names to cover absence of natural processes. Carnot, Clausius, and most of the classic writers on thermodynamics maintain an illusion of dealing with natural changes because they couch their comparisons of equilibria in terms of processes obeying, or usually obeying, thermal and caloric equations of state. The mathematics of thermostatics was made explicit and precise in 1875 by Gibbs, today often cited but apparently little read. He divided the subject into two parts: that based on formal manipulation of equations of state, and that based on true minimal principles. The true minimal principles are stronger: they imply not only the formal manipulations, which all amount to reinterpretation of the fact that the gradient vanishes at a minimum, and that partial differentiations commute and obey chain rules, but also conditions of stability and various consequent inequalities.

Planck in 1887 formulated the following inequality connecting differentials of energy E, temperature θ, and entropy H with the work W:

$$dE - \theta\,dH \leqq W, \tag{1}$$

a relation which he regarded as a summary of "all conclusions with regard to thermodynamic chemical changes, hitherto drawn by different authors in different ways...." Here, in general, no equation of state holds. Since differentials of independent variables are arbitrary quantities, the relation as it stands makes no sense at all. Planck claimed to deal with "any infinitesimal change" of "any system in nature," including "any homogeneous or heterogeneous system of bodies at a common temperature." Thus I believe he referred to *time rates* in *actual* processes. If so, we can find meaning for his postulate (1) if we replace it by

$$\dot{E} - \theta\dot{H} \leqq P, \tag{2}$$

where the dots indicate the time rates and where P is the rate of working of the mechanical forces.

Perhaps Planck meant by energy what we now call total energy, $E + K$, where K is the kinetic energy. The equation of balance of energy then is

$$\dot{K} + \dot{E} = P + Q, \tag{3}$$

where Q is the rate of increase of energy through nonmechanical effects such as heat conduction and radiation. If so, we can write Planck's postulate in the two forms:

$$\theta \dot{H} \geqslant \dot{E} + \dot{K} - P = Q, \tag{4}$$

each of which may be called the *Clausius–Planck inequality*.

The thermodynamics of deforming materials begins with gas dynamics. While this discipline goes back to Euler's day or earlier, the thermodynamic aspect of it was first made clear by Hadamard in his great treatise on waves in 1903. The total internal energy and total entropy of finite amounts $\mathscr{P}$ of a gas are additive set functions ("extensive variables" in Maxwell's terms):

$$E = \int_{\mathscr{P}} \varepsilon \, dm, \qquad H = \int_{\mathscr{P}} \eta \, dm, \tag{5}$$

and the corresponding densities ε and η, the specific internal energy and specific entropy, are assumed related to the density ρ by a local caloric equation of state:

$$f(\varepsilon, \eta, \rho) = 0. \tag{6}$$

Hadamard remarked that there was no basis in experiment for carrying over the static equations of state to "gases in more or less rapid motion." Nevertheless, from that day on, gas dynamics has rested upon free use of state, which enable all the formal apparatus of thermostatics to be incorporated thoughtlessly. The more recent "thermodynamics of irreversible processes," as developed by Eckart, Meixner, and others, rests upon transferring to more complicated phenomena the conceptual basis already familiar in gas dynamics and hence does not question the foundations. Hadamard's doubt remains. Why should static equations of state be valid in large and rapid deformations? More important than the doubt itself is the problem raised by a negative or conditioned answer. If a caloric equation of state is *not* valid, so that the classical thermostatic apparatus may *not* be applied to elements of mass in the deforming material, what *can* be said? In other words, what *are* the relations between thermal and mechanical quantities in severe and rapid deformations? More briefly, what are the laws of *thermodynamics*?

On the basis of the new continuum mechanics Coleman was able, last year, to formulate a thermodynamics of clarity, scope, and precision corresponding to Noll's theory of purely mechanical phenomena in simple materials.

Coleman's brilliant work rests on use of the most complicated and difficult aspects of functional analysis yet applied to continuum mechanics. However, the results he discovered are simple and easy to understand. Bowen and Wang, during their polite and silent attendance at some of the duller lectures at Bressanone in June, saw that a more general conception makes it possible to obtain the basic theory by use of no more than ordinary calculus as a tool. With their permission, I shall outline their procedure.

First we must agree on a starting point. As I have said for many years, disregarding the scoffs of those endowed with physical intuition, temperature and entropy join mass and place and time as primitive, undefined variables, described only by such properties as are laid down for them. Whenever anyone tries to do anything rational with temperature and entropy, some physicist rises to ask whether a temperature always exists, and how to define entropy. The same physicist if asked whether forces exist will reply that he is not interested in philosophical questions, and if asked how to define mass and force is likely to reply that mass is a measure of the quantity of matter in a body, while force represents a push or a pull in a given direction. Such a person ought to be satisfied if I answer that temperature is a measure of how hot a body is, while entropy represents how much heat has gone into a body at a given temperature. Just as we expect that the student in his elementary courses in physics has already acquired, regarding mechanics, some truths we need to reinforce and some errors we need to correct, so also we may presume that he has had the benefit of the vocabulary and confusion imparted by an elementary course in thermodynamics.

Thus we are free to speak of the temperature θ and the specific entropy η and to lay down for them, without further ado, conditions which embody and generalize the results of more than a century's experience with simple cases. In the equation of balance of energy (3), we now express Q in terms of an *efflux of energy* $\mathbf{h}$, intended to represent conduction of heat in broad form, and a *supply of energy*, q, intended to account for radiation and similar effects:

$$Q = \int_{\partial \mathscr{P}} \mathbf{h} \cdot \mathbf{n} \, da + \int_{\mathscr{P}} q \, dm. \qquad (7)$$

A local equivalent to the equation of energy is

$$\rho\dot{\varepsilon} = p + \operatorname{div}\mathbf{h} + \rho q, \tag{8}$$

where p is the density of internal working of the mechanical actions. As the basic postulate of irreversibility for materials in which the temperature need not be uniform, we lay down the *Clausius–Duhem inequality*:

$$\dot{H} = \frac{d}{dt}\int_{\mathscr{P}} \eta\, dm \geqslant \int_{\partial\mathscr{P}} \frac{\mathbf{h}}{\theta}\cdot\mathbf{n}\, da + \int_{\mathscr{P}} \frac{q}{\theta}\, dm, \tag{9}$$

or in local form

$$\rho\theta\dot{\eta} \geqslant \theta\operatorname{div}\left(\frac{\mathbf{h}}{\theta}\right) + \rho q. \tag{10}$$

Notice that the Clausius–Duhem inequality is not merely a local form of Planck's inequality, which would be

$$\rho\theta\dot{\eta} \geqslant \operatorname{div}\mathbf{h} + \rho q. \tag{11}$$

The two agree when θ is uniform at each time; if the classical heat conduction inequality holds, i.e.,

$$\frac{1}{\theta}\mathbf{h}\cdot\operatorname{grad}\theta \geqslant 0, \tag{12}$$

the Clausius–Duhem inequality implies the Clausius–Planck inequality. We shall regard Duhem's inequality as general. The work of Clausius, of course, formed the starting point for both, but it was Duhem who first saw the part played in the creation of entropy by heat conduction, which is the essence of the distinction here. The fully general inequality with the supply q included, first appeared in *The Classical Field Theories*. We shall return later to the relation between the two local inequalities.

The specific free energy ψ is defined by the classical formula

$$\psi \equiv \varepsilon - \eta\theta. \tag{13}$$

Guided by Coleman's results, we introduce the *internal dissipation, δ,* by the definition

$$\delta \equiv p - \rho\eta\dot{\theta} - \rho\dot{\psi} = p - \rho(\dot{\varepsilon} - \theta\dot{\eta}) = \rho\theta\dot{\eta} - \operatorname{div}\mathbf{h} - \rho q. \tag{14}$$

Since no differentials occur anywhere in this lecture, only the most confirmed classical thermodynamicist will confuse this δ with one of the dozens of variations of undefined functions of unspecified variables which are the hallmark of the formal structure of his subject. In classical thermostatics, since ψ is given by an equation of state, while p is a homogeneous linear function of the time rates of the state variables, $\delta = 0$, but in the more general case considered here, the internal dissipation is the amount by which internal working exceeds the rate of growth of internal energy less heat storage. Alternatively, δ/θ is the amount by which the entropy growth $\rho\dot\eta$ exceeds the quotient of nonmechanical power by temperature. With these notations, we obtain the fundamental *reduced dissipation inequality*:

$$\mathbf{h}\cdot\mathbf{g} \gneqq \theta\delta, \qquad \text{where} \quad \mathbf{g} \equiv \text{grad } \theta. \tag{15}$$

The word "reduced" refers to our having used the equations of balance of linear momentum, moment of momentum, and energy so as to eliminate the rates of working of all external sources: body forces, body couples, supply of energy, etc. When $\delta = 0$, the reduced dissipation inequality reduces to the familiar assertion that heat does not flow against a temperature gradient.

In passing, I comment that while the classical thermodynamicists were always embarrassed by heat conduction, finding it difficult to sneak this phenomenon into their theories through the back door, here we see heat conduction in its proper place as the central effect thermodynamics ought to describe.

Moreover, the statement that the internal dissipation is nonnegative,

$$\delta \gneqq 0, \tag{16}$$

is the local form of the Clausius–Planck inequality. Clearly it does *not* generally follow from or imply the Clausius–Duhem inequality.

Following earlier work by Coleman and Noll, we interpret dissipation inequalities as being *restrictions on constitutive equations*, on a par with the principles of material frame-indifference and local action. That is, we require that constitutive equations be of such a kind as to render the dissipation inequality satisfied *identically* by any deformation process kinematically possible. This requirement has long been laid down for the Navier–Stokes equations, for which the stress tensor $\mathbf{T}$ is of the form

$$\mathbf{T} = -\varpi(\rho)\mathbf{1} + \lambda(\text{tr } \mathbf{D})\mathbf{1} + 2\mu\mathbf{D}, \tag{17}$$

where $\mathbf{D}$ is the stretching tensor and where $\varpi(\rho)$ is derived from a local caloric equation of state by the standard thermodynamic formulas:

$$\varpi = -\partial_v\psi, \qquad \eta = -\partial_\theta\psi. \tag{18}$$

Then

$$\delta = \text{tr}(\mathbf{TD}) - \rho\eta\dot{\theta} - \rho\eta\dot{\theta} - \rho\dot{\psi}, \qquad \lambda(\text{tr}\,\mathbf{D})^2 + 2\mu\,\text{tr}\,\mathbf{D}^2. \qquad (19)$$

In this material, δ is unaffected by $\mathbf{g}$, so we can put $\mathbf{g} = \mathbf{0}$ in the reduced dissipation inequality and conclude that $\delta \geqq 0$. Necessary and sufficient conditions are the *Stokes–Duhem inequalities*:

$$\mu \geqq 0, \qquad 3\lambda + 2\mu \geqq 0. \qquad (20)$$

In this classical process, however, the dissipation inequality is brought in only at the end, without using it in full strength. In the spring of 1962 Noll constructed for our Encyclopedia article, then already four years in the writing, a development of finite hyperelasticity resting upon the dissipation inequality *alone*. A partial analysis based on the same idea was sent me by Green in 1962. In their path-breaking memoir of 1963, Coleman and Noll applied this same kind of reasoning to linearly viscous thermoelastic substances. Still more generally, this idea is the key to the thermodynamics of deformation.

Coleman's starting point for his general theory of 1964 was a set of constitutive equations for the free energy, entropy, stress, and heat flux as functionals of the deformation history and temperature history, dependent upon the temperature gradient $\mathbf{g} \equiv \text{grad}\,\theta$ as a parameter. A slightly more general starting point is:

$$\left.\begin{matrix} \psi \\ \eta \\ \mathbf{T} \\ \mathbf{h} \end{matrix}\right\} \text{are functionals of} \left\{\begin{matrix} \mathbf{F}^t \\ \theta^t \\ \mathbf{g}^t \end{matrix}\right. \qquad (21)$$

Schematically,

$$\Phi = \mathfrak{F}(\mathbf{F}^t, \theta^t, \mathbf{g}^t),$$

$$= \mathfrak{F}(\mathbf{F}_+{}^t, \theta_+{}^t, \mathbf{g}_+{}^t; \mathbf{F}(t), \theta(t), \mathbf{g}(t)), \qquad (22)$$

where $\mathbf{F}_+{}^t$, $\theta_+{}^t$, and $\mathbf{g}_+{}^t$ are the past histories $\mathbf{F}(t-s)$, $\theta(t-s)$, and $\mathbf{g}(t-s)$ for $s > 0$, while $\mathbf{F}(t)$, $\theta(t)$, and $\mathbf{g}(t)$ are the present values of $\mathbf{F}$, θ, and $\mathbf{g}$. Coleman assumed that for fixed $\mathbf{F}(t)$, $\theta(t)$, and $\mathbf{g}(t)$ the functional $\mathfrak{F}$ obeys the principle of fading memory in the sense made precise by Coleman and Noll in 1959. Among the results of Coleman's analysis is the proof that for a certain class of deformation-temperature histories, $\mathfrak{F}$ is therefore a continuously differentiable function of $\mathbf{F}(t)$, $\theta(t)$, and $\mathbf{g}(t)$, the *present* values of the deformation, the temperature, and its gradient.

Bowen and Wang have seen that this point is crucial in the whole theory. They consider *quasi-elastic response*, defined by the constitutive schema

$$\Phi = \mathfrak{f}(\theta, \mathbf{g}, \mathbf{F}, t) \tag{23}$$

where $\mathfrak{f}$ is a *function* and t is the time. A simple material as studied by Coleman is quasi-elastic in this sense, that if one considers a single, fixed particle and a single, fixed deformation-temperature history, its response is quasi-elastic if varying present values θ, $\mathbf{g}$, $\mathbf{F}$ are allowed. A different deformation-temperature past history for the same material again yields quasi-elastic repsonse, but, generally, a different function $\mathfrak{f}$. Noll in 1955 and Rivlin in 1956 had considered quasi-elastic response in the context of a special class of deformation histories, namely, a strain amount $\mathbf{F}$ occurring at time t. Here the idea is made more general in that an arbitrary deformation-temperature past history is allowed but held fixed. No comparisons are made between the results for different histories at the same particle, or for different particles subject to the same history.

Specifically, then, in accord with the principle of equipresence, Bowen and Wang consider quasi-elastic response described by the following equations:

$$\psi = \mathfrak{p}(\theta, \mathbf{g}, \mathbf{F}, t),$$

$$\eta = \mathfrak{h}(\theta, \mathbf{g}, \mathbf{F}, t),$$

$$\mathbf{T} = \mathfrak{T}(\theta, \mathbf{g}, \mathbf{F}, t), \tag{24}$$

$$\mathbf{h} = \mathfrak{h}(\theta, \mathbf{F}, t),$$

with the crucial assumption that all four functions are *continuously differentiable in all four arguments*. The class of simple materials with fading memory studied by Coleman is included as a special case. So are more general materials, including those whose response depends on the history of the temperature gradient. Since the past history is kept fixed while the present values of θ, $\mathbf{g}$, and $\mathbf{F}$ are varied, the essential requirements are, first, that the material's response be defined for discontinuous histories, and second, that the response change smoothly when the amount of the discontinuity is varied. In other words, the constitutive equation of the material must be compatible with infinitesimal wave motion and must not change irregularly in response to small differences of amplitude of the waves. Thus some materials are excluded. For example, the Navier–Stokes–Fourier fluids, or, more generally, the Rivlin–Ericksen materials, are not generally quasi-elastic, since for a given deformation history the stress in such a material is not determined by θ, **g**, and **F** at each time, being in fact affected by a number of time derivatives $\dot{\mathbf{F}}, \ddot{\mathbf{F}}, \ldots$.

With this general idea once grasped, the analysis is now easy, being essentially that given by Coleman and Noll in their paper of 1963. To make use of the dissipation inequality, we need an explicit form for p, the mechanical working. As suggested by the simple constitutive equations being used, we take the classical definition:

$$p = \mathrm{tr}(\mathbf{TD}),\tag{25}$$

but we remark that if more general concepts of stress and energy were used, as in the multipolar theory of Green and Rivlin, with a correspondingly more general definition of p the same method could be applied.

Substitution of the constitutive equations into the dissipation inequality yields

$$-\frac{1}{\theta}\mathbf{h}\cdot\mathbf{g} \leqslant \mathrm{tr}(\mathbf{T}\dot{\mathbf{F}}\mathbf{F}^{-1}) - \rho\eta\dot{\theta}$$

$$-\rho[\partial_t\mathfrak{p} + (\partial_{\mathbf{F}}\mathfrak{p})\dot{\mathbf{F}} + (\partial_\theta\mathfrak{p})\dot{\theta} + (\partial_{\mathbf{g}}\mathfrak{p})\dot{\mathbf{g}}].\tag{26}$$

That is,

$$-(\partial_{\mathbf{g}}\mathfrak{p})\dot{\mathbf{g}} - \rho(\partial_\theta\mathfrak{p} + \eta)\dot{\theta} + \mathrm{tr}\{[\mathbf{F}^{-1}\mathbf{T} - \rho(\partial_{\mathbf{F}}\mathfrak{p})^T]\dot{\mathbf{F}}\}$$

$$+\frac{1}{\theta}\mathbf{h}\cdot\mathbf{g} - \rho\,\partial_t\mathfrak{p} \geqslant 0.\tag{27}$$

A simple but not trivial construction shows that θ, **g**, **F**, $\dot{\theta}$, $\dot{\mathbf{g}}$, and $\dot{\mathbf{F}}$ may be given independent values compatible with the assumptions previously made. If we impose the principle of material frame-indifference on $\mathfrak{p}$, it is easy to show that $\mathbf{F}(\partial_{\mathbf{F}}\mathfrak{p})^T$ is a symmetric tensor. Therefore the coefficients of $\dot{\mathbf{g}}$, $\dot{\theta}$, and $\dot{\mathbf{F}}$ must vanish:

$$\partial_{\mathbf{g}}\mathfrak{p} = \mathbf{0},$$

$$\eta = -\partial_\theta\mathfrak{p},\tag{28}$$

$$\mathbf{T} = \rho\mathbf{F}(\partial_{\mathbf{F}}\mathfrak{p})^T.$$

Hence the internal dissipation is given by

$$\delta = -\rho\,\partial_t\mathfrak{p}.\tag{29}$$

The dissipation inequality therefore becomes

$$\frac{1}{\theta}\mathbf{h}\cdot\mathbf{g} \geqslant \delta.\tag{30}$$

Since by (28.1) and (29) the right-hand side of this inequality is independent of **g**, we may put **g** = **0** on the left-hand side and obtain

$$\delta \geqq 0. \tag{31}$$

These results constitute the *grand thermodynamic theorem* of Coleman, here seen to hold for any material with quasi-elastic response. The term "grand" refers not only to the quality of Coleman's ideas but also to the scope of the theorem, which shows that the classical structure, if properly recast, applies upon the grand scale of finite irreversible deformations in materials with long-range memory of a rather general kind. The four assertions of the theorem may be interpreted in turn.

1. For a given deformation history, the temperature gradient does not affect the free energy:

$$\psi = \mathfrak{p}(\theta, \mathbf{F}, t). \tag{32}$$

2. While memory effects generally contribute to the free energy, the entropy, and the stress, their influence upon the last two are *determined* by the result of their influence on the first, and by rules which are formally identical with those of classical thermostatics:

$$\eta = -\partial_\theta \mathfrak{p}, \qquad \mathbf{T} = \rho \mathbf{F} (\partial_{\mathbf{F}} \mathfrak{p})^T. \tag{33}$$

In particular, in isothermal motions the material behaves like a hyperelastic material with stored-energy function dependent upon the past history.

3. The internal dissipation is never negative:

$$\delta \geqq 0. \tag{34}$$

Thus the Clausius–Planck inequality in local form is a consequence of the Clausius–Duhem inequality, for quasi-elastic response. Equivalently,

$$-\delta = \rho \, \partial_t \mathfrak{p} \leqq 0. \tag{35}$$

Such change of free energy as may occur when the deformation and temperature are fixed is never an increase, as is only natural for an effect of memory on the available energy stored locally.

4. The magnitude of the internal dissipation delimits the possible obtuseness of **h** and grad θ:

$$\mathbf{h} \cdot \operatorname{grad} \theta \geqq -\theta\delta, \qquad \text{where} \quad \delta \geqq 0. \tag{36}$$

If δ is so large that $\theta\delta > |\mathbf{h}| \, |\operatorname{grad} \theta|$, no limitation results. To see that this result is in accord with expectation, recall that we can make δ arbitrarily large, even when the entropy is constant and the heat flux is solenoidal, by inserting a sufficiently great sink of energy, $\delta = -\rho q$.

Drawing off energy fast enough should indeed make it possible to force heat to run against whatever temperature gradient there may be. For a less artificial case, suppose that δ is large because the free energy is decreasing very rapidly from memory effects. Here, too, it is natural that the heat flux, which is, after all, a flux of energy, may be turned right against the temperature gradient.

With this mathematical structure, Coleman has been able to give a rational position to all the classic statements on reversible, irreversible, and cyclic processes, interpreting the thermodynamic potentials in turn, but I pass over this part of his work as being relatively straightforward.

The central part of Coleman's theory has been made, as I have explained to you, extremely simple and easy by use of Bowen and Wang's idea of quasi-elastic response. However, the range of applicability of the results to particular materials remains to be determined. Much of the difficult work of Coleman retains its importance as showing when the hypothesis of quasi-elastic response can be proved to hold because of material properties. In this sense, Coleman has found a position for the classical equations of state. Trivially and exactly, they hold for all materials in equilibrium, and they hold for those particular materials which exhibit no memory effects. Coleman has proved that they hold also in the limits of infinitely slow and infinitely fast processes occurring in materials with fading memory. For the former, let a deformation-temperature history $\mathbf{F}^t(s)$, $\theta^t(s)$ be given, and consider the retardation of this history, obtained by stretching the time scale in the past: $\mathbf{F}^t(\alpha s)$, $\theta^t(\alpha s)$ where α is a positive parameter. Coleman then proved that as $\alpha \to 0$, the classical thermostatic structure emerges asymptotically. In other words, the usual thermodynamics of volume elements is valid *in the limit of retardation.* Likewise, a fast process may be defined by holding the past histories $\mathbf{F}_+{}^t$ and $\theta_+{}^t$ constant, while changing discontinuously the present values $\mathbf{F}(t)$ and $\theta(t)$. In this *limit of rapid deformation,* the usual thermodynamics of volume elements again emerges. That is, in a material with fading memory the free-energy function approaches time-independent limits—generally different limits —over the sequences of histories corresponding to slow processes or to fast processes.

These conclusions may be illustrated by considering the behavior of a glass. A glass is but a simple fluid with long-range memory. Its flow behavior, in general, is elaborate, but if considered over a sufficiently long period, it reaches a configuration of equilibrium in accord with classical hydrostatics, with stored-energy function depending on the density alone. If studied sufficiently rapidly, however, it behaves like a material with a stored-energy function appropriate to an isotropic elastic solid. The various moduli of the glass, such as its shear modulus and its compressibility, depend on its previous history. Coleman's theory tells us that the behavior of a glass is typical of simple materials with fading memory, except, of course, that not all such materials are fluid or isotropic. As for the glass, the energy functions entering the caloric equations of state, in the two limit cases, are different, and they depend upon the deformation-temperature history.

As far as concerns purely mechanical phenomena in homogeneous bodies, what in the thermodynamic literature is called a "Gibbs relation" corresponds to the theory of finite thermo-elasticity in continuum mechanics. We can say that the theory of finite elastic strain emerges from Coleman's thermodynamics in four different ways: as the general theory of equilibrium, as a theory of a particularly simple class of materials, as an asymptotic limit for all materials with fading memory in very slow processes, and as a similar limit for all such materials in very fast processes. In the two limit cases, corrections of arbitary order can be calculated if the free-energy functional is known. The first-order corrections are given by linear integral operators applied to the deformation-temperature history, as to be expected from Coleman and Noll's scheme of approximation in the purely mechanical theory.

We see that thermodynamics, after its slumber of half a century, has joined the older science of mechanics and the younger science of electro-magnetism as a fully formulated mathematical discipline, capable on the one hand of providing definite mathematical problems to be solved in order that application to cases be made, ready on the other hand for generalization to more elaborate phenomena such as chemical reactions and electromechanics. As with the organization of classical mechanics long ago, the way seems easier in retrospect than it did beforehand, and the problem was much the same for each. It was necessary to separate what was special, if true, from what was general; above all, to recognize what a constitutive equation can do and can not do.

In looking back upon the enormous growth since 1962 in our understanding of thermo-energetic effects, account must be taken also of the enlightenment gained from the detailed, rigorous theories of the thermo-*statics* of continua constructed by Coleman and Noll in 1958–1959 and still partly unpublished. For thermo*dynamics*, the men responsible in greater or lesser degree, to the best of my knowledge, and in the order of their work in it, are Noll, A. E. Green, Coleman, Mizel, Bowen, and Wang, and among them, certainly, we must regard Coleman as the principal.

An Alternative to the Continuum—the Aggregate as a Geometrical Basis for the Deformation Tensor and for Theories of Liquids

F. W. SMITH

Division of Mechanical Engineering
National Research Council of Canada
Ottawa, Ontario, Canada

The divergence between continuum mechanics and the molecular theory of liquids raises the question of defining deformation in a manner cognate to molecular theory. The procedure described here is to regard a rheological body as an "aggregate"—a set of nonoverlapping bodies in Euclidean space. The concept of a "displacement tensor," defined in terms of the motion of the surfaces involved, is used to show that a diagonalized deformation tensor for an aggregate can be resolved into matrices representing "inherent deformation" and "flow deformation." Potential applications in rheology and the theory of the activation volume of liquids are briefly mentioned.

1. Introduction

The divergence between continuum mechanics and the molecular theory of liquids arises in part because the properties of the physical continuum, and the concept of deformation defined in its terms, provide little basis for discussing the behavior of a single molecule and its immediate environment in a flowing liquid. The question arises as to whether alternative definitions of deformation exist which are more cognate to molecular processes.

The possibility of finding novel ways of looking at the properties of liquids was suggested by the theory of liquids of Bernal.[1-4] In this theory the study of purely geometric properties of such irregular aggregates as "random close-packed" masses of equal spheres explains certain properties of real liquids and gives a vivid impression of many other of their properties. In an attempt to use Bernal's theory to develop a treatment of liquid viscosity, a preceding paper[5] gave a relation between the

macroscopic rate of shear and the rates of molecular processes in the
Bernal liquid. In the process, a concept of "volume production,"
expressing the rate at which cavities between the spheres were created
and destroyed, was used empirically. In this paper, an attempt is made
to generalize this approach by describing the deformation of a liquid
of molecules of arbitrary shape, and by providing an algebraic basis for
"volume production," in a concept termed the "displacement tensor."

2. The General Aggregate

The geometrical model of a rheological body used here is selected as
being the most general possible. It consists of a set of closed surfaces,
each representing a molecule, moving in Euclidean space. These surfaces, or "members," may move and deform arbitrarily, may touch or
pack to fill space, but they do not overlap. This system is termed the
"general aggregate." The intention is to find a way of describing the
flow or deformation of an aggregate in terms of the way the surfaces of
the members sweep out volume, i.e., the way points of the Euclidean
space move through the surfaces of the members.

The motion (including rotation and deformation) of a surface in
Euclidean space can be represented in two ways. Firstly, as a pointwise
homeomorphism, where the motion of each point in the surface is considered, and secondly, as a surfacewise homeomorphism, where only the
displacement of the surface is considered. The latter is a more general
concept and seems preferable in discussing the "surface" of a molecule;
it will be used here.

3. "Inherent" and "Flow" Deformation of an Aggregate

In this section, a tentative treatment is proposed to describe the
deformation of an aggregate, by way of outlining a possible way of
reconciling macroscopic and molecular concepts.

The system described consists of a macroscopic closed surface $\mathscr{S}$
which encloses a large number of individual members of the aggregate.
As a concrete example, the macroscopic surface could be the small
volume element frequently considered in flow problems (save that it
seems necessary to restrict this to an initially spherical element), while
the members of the aggregate could be lubricant molecules.

We assume that this system undergoes a finite homogeneous deformation in Euclidean space, and that the deformation is characterized by
a deformation gradient F, which can be decomposed into a rotation R

followed by a left strain tensor W, the latter being symmetrical[6]:

$$F = WR \tag{1}$$

The tensor W can then be diagonalized by rotating its axes by an appropriate rotation tensor T

$$D = TWT^T \tag{2}$$

$$F = T^TDTR \tag{3}$$

where D is a strictly diagonal strain matrix.

We now connect with the concept of deformation as volume displacement by considering the integral geometry of the surface $\mathscr{S}$. If the volume enclosed by $\mathscr{S}$ is $\mathscr{V}$, the average length L_{11} of $\mathscr{S}$ in a given direction is given by

$$L_{11} = \mathscr{V}/A_{11} \tag{4}$$

where A_{11} is the projected area of $\mathscr{S}$ onto a plane normal to the given direction. The deformation F can then be said to change the average length of $\mathscr{S}$ along each of the three axes of D, and we can write

$$\begin{pmatrix} D_{11} & \cdot & \cdot \\ \cdot & D_{22} & \cdot \\ \cdot & \cdot & D_{33} \end{pmatrix} = \begin{pmatrix} L_{11}^{(2)}/L_{11}^{(1)} & \cdot & \cdot \\ \cdot & L_{22}^{(2)}/L_{22}^{(1)} & \cdot \\ \cdot & \cdot & L_{33}^{(2)}/L_{33}^{(1)} \end{pmatrix} \tag{5}$$

where the superscripts (1) and (2) refer to the average lengths before and after the deformation, respectively.

Next, we replace D by a related matrix V which gives not the change in length, but the volume which can be said to be swept out by the surface $\mathscr{S}$ along each of the three principal axes of D.

$$V = \begin{pmatrix} \int_{(1)}^{(2)} (\mathscr{V}/L_{11})\,dL_{11} & \cdot & \cdot \\ \cdot & \int_{(1)}^{(2)} (\mathscr{V}/L_{22})\,dL_{22} & \cdot \\ \cdot & \cdot & \int_{(1)}^{(2)} (\mathscr{V}/L_{33})\,dL_{33} \end{pmatrix} \tag{6}$$

where the terms $\mathscr{V}/L_{11}$, etc., are the projected areas and the integration proceeds throughout the deformation F; by selecting $\mathscr{S}$ as spherical, V represents only deformation and not rotation of the system. The matrix V will be termed the displacement matrix for the deformation. Its characteristic is that its three scalars represent the magnitude of D, and its trace gives the scalar volume change of $\mathscr{S}$ during the deformation. In infinitesimal deformation, V becomes simply related to D:

$$V \rightarrow \mathscr{V}(D - 1), \qquad \text{as} \quad D \rightarrow 1 \tag{7}$$

For present purposes, the significance of V is in the possibility of relating it to molecular processes. For each member of the aggregate we can calculate a local matrix v representing its volume displacement along the axes of D for the generally nonaffine motion it undergoes while $\mathscr{S}$ undergoes the deformation F. The strictly diagonal components of v may be written, analogously to (6)

$$v_{rr} = \int (\nu / l_{rr}) \, dl_{rr} \qquad \text{(no sum)} \tag{8}$$

where ν is the volume of the individual member concerned, and l_{rr} is average length along the given axis.

Finally, we can write a displacement matrix which is the sum of all the displacement matrices of the individual molecules enclosed by the surface $\mathscr{S}$, and term it the "inherent" displacement matrix:

$$V^{\text{inh}} = \sum v \tag{9}$$

Descriptively, it represents the deformation of individual molecules and their mean rotation relative to the axes of D; one would expect it to be associated with a viscoelastic or energy storage effect; it would be zero for the flow of a liquid of spherical molecules. It is evidently less than the displacement matrix V of the external surface $\mathscr{S}$. Therefore, we can term their difference a "flow" displacement matrix, and write an equation for the finite deformation of an aggregate:

$$V = V^{\text{inh}} + V^{\text{flow}} \tag{10}$$

4. Conclusions

If it can be assumed that the treatment given here in terms of diagonal matrices can be extended to a frame-indifferent tensor form, then among possible applications of the preceding scheme may be the following. Firstly, the deformation tensor, at least in the case of rheological bodies consisting of discrete molecules, can be resolved into two components of different physical insignificance. The inherent deformation expressed by V^{inh} can be thought of as a generalization of the concept of molecular alignment in flow, as measured, for instance, by optical birefringence. The need for such a generalization in the case of the behavior of lubricants under high stress has recently been mentioned.[7]

Secondly, the concept of "activation volume" as used in the rate theory of liquid viscosity may be elucidated. The activation process is the growth of an intermolecular cavity which can be treated in the present terms as the motion of a volume enclosed by a closed surface, and represented by a displacement tensor. On this basis the "magnitude" of the local activation volume for a particular molecular process, and possibly also the molar activation volume for a particular liquid, should be represented by three scalars rather than by one. A likely consequence is for instance, that in calculating the effect of stress on liquid viscosity by means of rate theories of the type used previously,[5] the hydrostatic stress and the shear stress may enter into the activation energy each multiplied by a differently valued activation volume.

REFERENCES

1. J. D. Bernal, *Nature* **183**, 141 (1959).
2. J. D. Bernal, *Nature* **185**, 68 (1960).
3. J. D. Bernal, *Proc. Roy. Soc. (London)* **A280**, 299 (1964).
4. J. D. Bernal, The geometry of the structure of liquids, *in* "Liquids: Structure, Properties, Solid Interactions," (Th. J. Hughel, ed.). Elsevier, Amsterdam, 1965.
5. F. W. Smith, *Can. J. Phys.* **42**, 304 (1964).
6. W. Noll, *Arch. Rational Mech. Anal. (Berlin)* **2**, 197 (1962).
7. R. A. Burton, The thermodynamics of a viscoelastic film under shear and compression, *in* "Elastohydrodynamic Lubrication," *Inst. Mech. Engrs. (London)*, Symposium at Leeds (1965).

Shear Wave Propagation in Birefringent Viscoelastic Liquids of Low Rigidity and Low Viscosity †

GEORGE B. THURSTON

Physics Department
Oklahoma State University
Stillwater, Oklahoma

Utilizing the optical birefringence induced by shearing deformation of viscoelastic liquids it is possible to carry out direct quantitative measurements of the progression of a shear wave in the liquid. From measurements of the amplitude and phase of the optical effect vs propagation distance, values of the attenuation and phase constants of the medium are obtained. From these, a complex coefficient of viscosity is determined. An improved optical detection scheme permits measurements as near to the shear wave source as 100 microns with a field resolution of approximately 10 microns. It is thus possible to carry out measurements for liquids of viscosity near that of water and having very low rigidity. A theoretical model for a dilute suspension of rigid macromolecules of ellipsoidal shape is described and measured values are compared with the theory. This is done for an aqueous suspension of colloidal alumina, Dupont Baymal, with good general agreement as to frequency and temperature dependence of the propagation characteristics. Measured values are also presented for a polyethylene oxide polymer in combination with Baymal in water.

1. Introduction

The characteristics of shear wave propagation are closely related to the viscoelastic properties of the supporting medium. Working particularly with liquids which exhibit optical birefringence when in shear, it is possible to use optical methods to monitor the progression of the shear wave. Studies of this type have been carried out previously by Ferry and Helders[1] for a solution of rodlike intermediate polymers of bovine fibrinogen, by Helders *et al.*[2] for concentrated solutions of

† This work was supported by Acoustics Programs, Office of Naval Research, U.S. Navy.

sodium desoxyribonucleate (SDNA), and by Thurston and Schrag[3] for a solution of polystyrene in Aroclor 1248 and for a colloidal suspension of aqueous milling yellow.

In the case of materials exhibiting relatively high viscosity, the shear wavelength is relatively large and when accompanied by substantial rigidity gives relatively low attenuation rate. Hence, the propagating wave persists in space permitting relative ease of measurement of the progression of the wave. On the other hand, for liquids of viscosity near that of water and having small rigidity, the wavelength and attenuation rate become such as to give a relatively short range of propagation and to correspondingly limit the measurements. For example, for water at 25°C at 100 cps, the attenuation factor α and phase factor β are equal, and $\alpha = \beta = 186$/cm. This gives a shear wave length of 0.033 cm. It follows that in each 330 microns (μ) of propagation, the amplitude decreases by a factor of 541. Under these conditions, carrying out direct observations of the wave propagation becomes difficult.

By an optical improvement in a system of measurement previously described,[3] measurements have been successfully carried out for water-like liquids. The particular liquid studied is an aqueous suspension of alumina (AlOOH) in the form of a colloidal fibrilar particle. This material is marketed under the trade name Baymal by E. I. Du Pont de Nemours and Co., Inc. Some of its properties have been previously described.[4,5] The alumina fibrils which make up the particle are approximately 5 mμ in diameter and 100 mμ in length. The final particle in aqueous suspension may be more the order of 600 mμ in length. Even at low concentrations, this particle provides sufficient optical anisotropy in shear to permit measurement of the shear wave propagation by the birefringence effect.

Baymal particles in aqueous suspension behave as rigid ellipsoidal particles. The mechanical properties of such a system of particles have been treated theoretically for sinusoidal shear by Cerf.[6] General optical properties of the suspension for steady shear flow have been described by Peterlin and Stuart.[7] More recently the close relation between the optical birefringence and the viscoelastic properties has been studied both theoretically and experimentally by Cerf and Thurston,[8] the relation between the optical birefringence and the instantaneous stress-strain rate being given for both rigid and flexible macromolecules in solution. However, such details are not necessary to the method of study of shear waves described herein as it is sufficient that a linear relationship between birefringence and shear gradient in the field exists. This assures that the progression in magnitude and phase of the observed birefringence is simply related to the progression of the mechanical parameters of the shear wave.

2. Propagation Equations

The propagating wave is assumed to be a plane shear wave which obeys the differential wave equation for sinusoidal waves

$$\eta^*\left(\frac{\partial^2 \dot{\xi}}{\partial x^2}\right) = \rho\left(\frac{\partial \dot{\xi}}{\partial t}\right) \tag{1}$$

where

$$\eta^* = \eta \exp[-i\varphi_\eta] \tag{2}$$

is the complex coefficient of viscosity which appears in the stress, T, strainrate, $(\partial \dot{\xi}/\partial x)$, relation

$$T = \eta^*\left(\frac{\partial \dot{\xi}}{\partial x}\right), \tag{3}$$

$\dot{\xi}$ is the particle velocity of the wave which is propagating in the $+x$ direction, and ρ is the density of the medium. The solution to (1) for a simple sinusoidal wave of radian frequency ω is

$$\dot{\xi} = \dot{\xi}_0 \exp[i(\omega t - \gamma x)] \tag{4}$$

where

$$\gamma = (\beta - i\alpha) \tag{5}$$

is the complex propagation constant, β is the phase constant and is $(2\pi/\lambda_s)$ when λ_s is the shear wavelength, and α is the attenuation constant. From (1) one then obtains

$$\gamma^2 = -(i\omega\rho)/\eta^*. \tag{6}$$

From this the viscosity and propagation constants are related by

$$\beta = \left(\frac{\rho\omega}{\eta}\right)^{1/2} \cos\left[\left(\frac{\varphi_\eta}{2}\right) - \left(\frac{\pi}{4}\right)\right] \tag{7}$$

$$\alpha = \left(\frac{\rho\omega}{\eta}\right)^{1/2} \sin\left[\left(\frac{\varphi_\eta}{2}\right) - \left(\frac{\pi}{4}\right)\right], \tag{8}$$

or inversely,

$$\eta = (\rho\omega)/(\alpha^2 + \beta^2) \tag{9}$$

$$\tan\varphi_\eta = \frac{1}{2}\left[\left(\frac{\beta}{\alpha}\right) - \left(\frac{\alpha}{\beta}\right)\right]. \tag{10}$$

The optical birefringence induced in the medium by the sinusoidal shear wave is related to the velocity gradient by

$$\Delta n^* = S^* \left(\frac{\partial \dot{\xi}}{\partial x}\right) \tag{11}$$

where Δn^* is the complex birefringence, this being the instantaneous difference between the indices of refraction along the optical axes of the medium and

$$S^* = S \exp[i\theta_s] \tag{12}$$

is a complex mechano-optic factor.

The change in polarization of collimated, circularly polarized light on passage through the medium at right angles to the direction of shear wave propagation serves to relate the birefringence to the shear wave propagation. Figure 1 shows the optical polarization conditions employed. Right circularly polarized light is incident upon the medium and

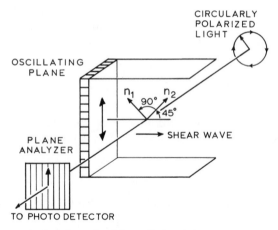

FIG. 1   Arrangement of elements of the optical and shear wave systems showing wave propagation directions and optical polarization conditions.

propagates tangent to the oscillating plane. The shear wave propagating at right angles to the optical transmission produces optic axes in the medium which lie along the directions of the principal stresses due to the shear wave in the medium. The optical indices are noted as n_1 and n_2, the instantaneous difference between these being the birefringence Δn. A vertically oriented plane analyzer is used to analyze the modification of the circularly polarized light. A photomultiplier then serves as the final detector for the transmitted light. If the optical retardation is small, say less than $\frac{1}{12}$ of an optical wavelength, then the photoresponse is given by[3]

$$I \cong I_0[1 + (2\pi/\lambda_{op}) \Delta n \, L] \tag{13}$$

where λ_{op} is the optical wave length, L is the optical path length, Δn is the instantaneous value of the birefringence, and I_0 is the quiescent photocurrent background. By substitution of the shear velocity (4) into the birefringence relation (11), and substituting the real part of the bi-refringence into (13), the equation for the propagation of the photo-response becomes

$$I = I_0 + I_1 \cos(\omega t + \sigma) \tag{14}$$

where

$$I_1/(I_0 \dot{\xi}_0) = (2\pi/\lambda_{op})SL(\beta^2 + \alpha^2)^{1/2} \exp[-\alpha x]$$
$$= [\text{a constant}] \cdot \exp[-\alpha x] \tag{15}$$

and

$$\sigma = -\beta x + \pi/2 - \tan^{-1}(\alpha/\beta) + \theta_s$$
$$= -\beta x + [\text{a constant}]. \tag{16}$$

Thus it is seen that by measuring the alternating component of the photo-response as a function of the propagation distance, x, the attenuation factor α is given by (15), and the phase factor β is given by (16).

3. Experimental Apparatus

The arrangement of the optical and mechanical apparatus used in carrying out shear wave propagation measurements is shown in Fig. 2. The supporting structure for the system, B, is a Spindler and Hoyer

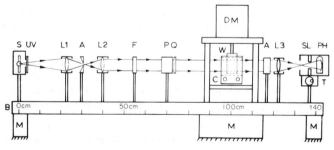

FIG. 2   Arrangement of optical and mechanical apparatus used for shear wave propagation measurements.

optical bench supported on each end and in the center by steel masses, M. These masses serve to minimize mechanical vibration of the overall system. The optical system covers approximately 140 cm of the bench, the shear wave generating apparatus being near the 100 cm mark. Tracing the optical system, S, is the light source which is an Osram HBO 100W/2 super pressure mercury lamp activated by a George W. Gates power supply. This arc source is approximately 0.3 mm in diameter. The arc lamp output is passed through an ultraviolet filter, UV, and then through the lens, L1, a 50-mm focal length, F4.5 lens. The image of S is then formed by L1 near the aperture, A, to give a reduction in the effective source size to approximately 0.05 mm in diameter. The lens L2, a 100-mm focal length F3.5 lens, serves to give a collimated optical field. Collimated light then passes through the interference filter, F, having a peak transmission at 5790 Å. The elements PQ are a combination of a Glan Thompson polarizer and a quarter wave plate so oriented as to give right circularly polarized light. The light then passes through a thin glass window into the brass cell, C, containing the liquid supporting the shear wave. The brass body of the cell is perforated with channels through which a temperature controlling liquid is circulated. The control liquid is supplied by a Haake constant temperature circulator. The temperature of the liquid under study is monitored by a thermistor which is immersed therein.

The oscillating plane W, is of 1-mm-thick black glass, 1 inch long, along the optical path. The plane is activated by an electrodynamic driver, D, the motion being monitored by an electrodynamic pickup, M. After the collimated light passes through the region of liquid near W which is supporting the shear wave it then leaves the cell C by a thin exit window. It then passes through a plane optical analyzer, A, a Glan Thompson prism. From this it passes through a lens, L3, a 75-mm focal length F4.5 converging lens, and then to a thin receiving slit, SL, of width 0.0038 cm in the shear wave propagation direction and 1 cm in height. Following the receiving slit is a light diffuser and photomultiplier, PH, RCA type 6328. The slit and photomultiplier assembly is supported by a traveling microscope stage, T, which is to carry the slit so as to scan the image plane of the lens L3. In this image plane the events in the shear wave field are magnified by a factor of 1.8. Thus the receiving slit sees a section of the shear wave field approximately 0.002 cm wide by 0.6 cm high.

The basic technique of measurement is that of measuring the amplitude and phase of the photocurrent as a function of the position of the receiving slit, x. Then from the space rate of change of this amplitude and phase, the propagation and phase factors are determined. For the relatively short propagation range of shear waves in liquids of low viscosity and low rigidity, the primary measurement problem is that of being able to measure meaningful photocurrents very near to the oscillating plane. The limitation here is determined by the diffraction of light by the plane which thus disturbs the otherwise simple rectilinear propagation in the collimated field. The primary function of the lens L3 is to minimize this optical diffraction.

The effect of the lens L3 is best seen with reference to Fig. 3. L3 is positioned so as to form an image at the receiving slit position of the fluid near the center of the oscillating plane. It is found that in this way

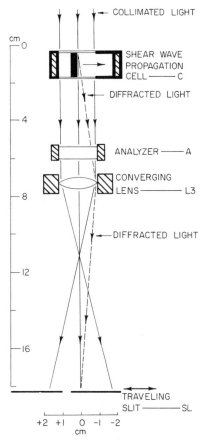

FIG. 3 Optical conditions for minimizing diffraction effects at the receiving slit.

the diffraction pattern is concentrated to give a minimum of disturbance to the collimated optical field as seen in the plane of the receiving slit. The diffraction pattern thus obtained is shown in Fig. 4. The results shown are for a 0.3% suspension of Baymal in water at a temperature of 25°C. The diffraction pattern shown is simply the spacial variation of the quiescent photocurrent, I_0. Also shown are the amplitude and phase of the photocurrent, for a 50 cps shear wave. It is estimated that the

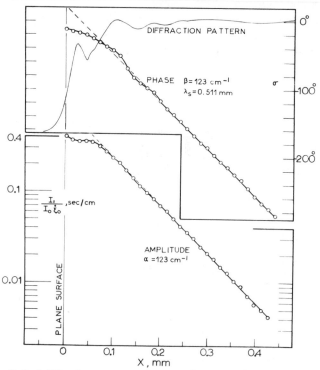

FIG. 4   Optical diffraction pattern and propagation curves for 0.3% Baymal in water at 25°C and 50 cps.

spacial resolution in the shear wave field is approximately 0.01 mm for these measurements. It is seen that the character of the inflections in the diffraction pattern are reflected in the propagation curves. In order to obtain a linear progression of phase and a logarithmic progression of amplitude, it is necessary to analyze only the region more distant than 0.1 mm from the surface of the oscillating plane. In the region nearer the plane the complications of optical diffraction give rise to some more complex relations between the photoresponse and the shear wave field.

In the linear regions of Fig. 4, the shear wavelength given is 0.511 mm and α and β are approximately 123/cm, where the value for water would be 132.5/cm. Thus it is seen that under these conditions of frequency and temperature direct measurements can be made on waterlike liquids while still avoiding the problems associated with optical diffraction.

4. Theoretical Model for a Suspension of Rigid Ellipsoidal Particles

The mechanical properties have been derived by Cerf[6] for a suspension of rigid particles shaped as ellipsoids of revolution, monodisperse, noninteracting as in a dilute suspension of macromolecules. Cerf's results may be expressed in terms of an equivalent mechanical model per unit volume of material. Figure 5 shows the model which relates the shearing stress T and strain rate $(\partial \dot{\xi}/\partial x)$, these determining η^* by

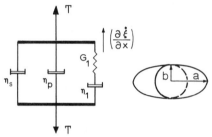

FIG. 5   Mechanical model for unit volume of liquid suspension of ellipsoidal particles.

Eq. (3). The elements of the model may be designated in several possible ways. Two of the more useful formulations are as follows:

$$\eta_p = C_{vol}H(p)\eta_s$$
$$\eta_1 = C_{vol}B(p)\eta_s \tag{17}$$
$$G_1 = 6D_rC_{vol}B(p)\eta_s$$

where η_s is the viscosity of the solvent; C_{vol} is the volume of solute per unit volume of solution; p is the axial ratio for the ellipsoid of rotation and is greater than 1 for a prolate (elongated) ellipsoid, equal to 1 for a sphere, less than one for an oblate (flattened) ellipsoid; D_r is the rotary diffusion coefficient of the particle; $H(p)$ and $B(p)$ are dimensionless functions of the axial ratio p. For p large, say greater than 5, the functions $H(p)$ and $B(p)$ for the prolate ellipsoid are given by

$$H(p) \cong \tfrac{8}{5} + (p^2/15)(\ln 2p - \tfrac{3}{2})$$
$$B(p) \cong (p^2/5)/(\ln 2p - \tfrac{1}{2}). \tag{18}$$

For p small, say less than 0.2, $H(p)$ and $B(p)$ for the oblate ellipsoid are given by

$$H(p) \cong \tfrac{4}{9} + [4/(3\pi p)]$$

$$B(p) \cong 4/(5\pi p). \tag{19}$$

The rotary diffusion constant is given by

$$D_r \cong \left(\frac{3kT}{16\pi\eta_s a^3}\right)(-1 + 2\ln 2p), \qquad \text{for} \quad p \gg 1, \qquad \text{or}$$

$$\tag{20}$$

$$D_r \cong (3kT)/(32\eta_s b^3), \qquad \text{for} \quad p \ll 1,$$

where k is Boltzmann's constant and T is the absolute temperature in degrees Kelvin. Alternate expressions for the elements of the model that are perhaps more directly relatable to experimental data are

$$\eta_p = \left(\frac{1}{1 + B/H}\right)(\eta_0 - \eta_s)$$

$$\eta_1 = \left(\frac{1}{1 + H/B}\right)(\eta_0 - \eta_s) \tag{21}$$

$$G_1 = (3kTC_{\text{vol}})/(5v)$$

where η_0 is the viscosity at zero frequency, and v is the volume of one particle.

For p large and the particles elongated, Eqs. (18) give $B \cong 3H$, and Eqs. (21) become

$$\eta_p \cong (1/4)(\eta_0 - \eta_s)$$

$$\eta_1 \cong (3/4)(\eta_0 - \eta_s) \tag{22}$$

$$G_1 \cong D_r(9/2)(\eta_0 - \eta_s).$$

From the model, the complex viscosity coefficient is

$$\eta^* = T/(\partial \dot\xi/\partial x) = \eta_s + \eta_p + \eta_1/(1 + i\omega t) \tag{23}$$

where the relaxation time τ is given by

$$\tau = \eta_1/G_1 = 1/(6D_r), \tag{24}$$

and by determination of the magnitude η and the viscosity angle φ_η from rationalization of (23), the propagation constants for shear waves are given by (7) and (8).

It is desired to examine the frequency and temperature dependences to be derived from this model. First, it is noted from (17) that the ratio of the steady flow viscosity to the solvent viscosity is

$$(\eta_0/\eta_s) = 1 + C_{vol}(H + B) \tag{25}$$

and this is independent of temperature as long as the axial ratio and volume concentration remain unchanged. Next, consider the relaxation time, τ, as given by (24). In view of the temperature dependence of D_r, τ will be primarily temperature dependent through the ratio of (T/η_s). Thus, if one arbitrarily selects a reference temperature, T_0, expressed in degrees Kelvin and for which the relaxation time is τ_0, then the relaxation time τ at any temperature will be given by

$$\tau = \tau_0 \left(\frac{\eta_s}{\eta_{so}}\right)\left(\frac{T_0}{T}\right) \tag{26}$$

where η_{so} is the viscosity of the solvent at the reference temperature. Using these equations, general expressions for the frequency and temperature dependence of η^* may be stated as

$$\frac{\eta(T)}{\eta_0(T_0)} = \left(\frac{\eta_s}{\eta_{so}}\right)\left\{Q^2 + (1 - Q^2)\left[1 + (\omega\tau_0)^2\left(\frac{\eta_s}{\eta_{so}}\right)^2\left(\frac{T_0}{T}\right)^2\right]^{-1}\right\}^{1/2} \tag{27}$$

and

$$\tan \varphi_\eta = \frac{(\omega\tau_0)(\eta_s/\eta_{so})(T_0/T)}{1 + [Q/(1 - Q)][1 + (\omega\tau_0)^2(\eta_s/\eta_{so})^2(T_0/T)^2]} \tag{28}$$

where Q is a factor, independent of frequency and temperature, given by

$$Q = \left(\frac{\eta_s}{\eta_0} + \frac{H}{B}\right)\bigg/\left(1 + \frac{H}{B}\right) \tag{29}$$

and $\eta_0(T_0)$ is the steady flow viscosity at the reference temperature.

From (27) and (28) the temperature dependence and frequency dependence of the propagation factors may be determined. By substitution into (7) and (8), one obtains

$$\frac{\beta}{K_0} = \left[\frac{(\rho/\rho_0)(\omega\tau_0)}{\eta/\eta_0(T_0)}\right]^{1/2} \cos\left(\frac{\varphi_\eta}{2} - \frac{\pi}{4}\right) \tag{30}$$

and

$$\frac{\alpha}{K_0} = \left[\frac{(\rho/\rho_0)(\omega\tau_0)}{\eta/\eta_0(T_0)}\right]^{1/2} \sin\left(\frac{\varphi_\eta}{2} - \frac{\pi}{4}\right) \tag{31}$$

where K_0 is a constant given by

$$K_0 = \left[\frac{\rho_0}{\tau_0\eta_0(T_0)}\right]^{1/2}. \tag{32}$$

George B. Thurston

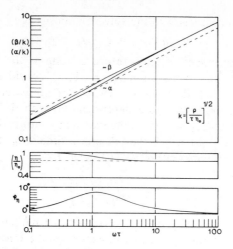

FIG. 6   Frequency dependence of β, α, η, and φ for the special ratio $\eta_0/\eta_s = 1.5$.

Equations (27) and (28) may be conveniently used to determine the frequency dependence of η and φ_η and (30) and (31) may be similarly used to determine β and α. This is simply done by taking ($T = T_0$) in which case the ratios (ρ/ρ_0), (T_0/T), and (η_s/η_{s0}) become 1 and since the reference temperature T_0 is arbitrary, one simply obtains frequency

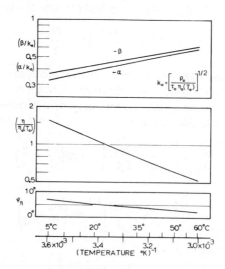

FIG. 7   Temperature dependence of β, α, η, and φ_η for the special case of a water solvent, $T_0 = 298°K$, $\eta_0/\eta_s = 1.5$, and $(\omega\tau_0) = 0.374$.

dependent equations. In this case, (η/η_0), φ_η, (β/K) and (α/K) are functions of the product (ωt) only for a given ratio of solution viscosity at zero frequency to solvent viscosity, (η_0/η_s). Figure 6 shows the results of a set of calculations of these four factors for $(\eta_0/\eta_s = 1.5)$ for a range of $(\omega\tau)$ covering the relaxation region.

In order to examine the temperature dependence according to Eqs. (27), (28), (30), and (31) additional factors must be specified. These include selecting a reference temperature T_0, then the solvent viscosity at this temperature η_{s0}, and finally a value for $(\omega\tau_0)$. Figure 7 shows calculations for a reference temperature of 25°C, for water, for $(\omega\tau_0) = 0.374$, and $(\eta_0/\eta_s = 1.5)$. These values were used in order to correspond to an experimental condition to be described.

5. Experimental Measurements

Measurements have been carried out for several aqueous suspensions of Baymal as functions of both frequency and temperature. Figures 8 and 9 show the results obtained for a 2% weight concentration of Baymal in water. Figure 8 shows the effect of frequency at 25°C on β, α, η and

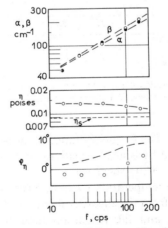

FIG. 8 Measured frequency dependence of β, α, η, and φ_η for 2% Baymal in water at 25°C. The dashed lines are theoretical curves from Fig. 6.

φ_η. The broad dashed lines are the values computed from the model and as are given in Fig. 6. It is seen that the character of the data is in general agreement with the theory. It is to be noted that in cases such as this, where $(\alpha \cong \beta)$, the measurement errors have a larger effect upon φ_η than upon η. The precision of the α and β determination here is

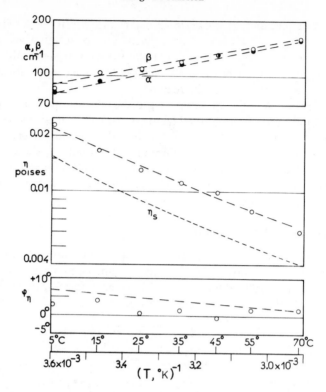

FIG. 9   Measured temperature dependence of β, α, η, and φ_η for 2% Baymal in water at 50 cps. The dashed lines are theoretical curves from Fig. 7.

approximately $\pm 5\%$. The frequency range of measurement is limited on the low frequency end by optical sensitivity and in the high end by the range of propagation of the shear wave.

Figure 9 shows the temperature effect at 50 cps for this same sample. The dashed lines are from the theoretical curves of Fig. 7. The reference temperature is 25°C, and the relaxation time at that temperature is estimated to be 0.00119 sec, which gives $(\omega\tau_0) = 0.374$. This value of relaxation time is about half of that found for very low concentrations, thus indicating possibly substantial particle interaction at 2% concentration.

Measurements were also carried out at a lower concentration of Baymal. Figures 10 and 11 are for a 0.3% weight concentration. Here it is seen that the behavior is very close to that of water, with no appreciable elastic effects in evidence.

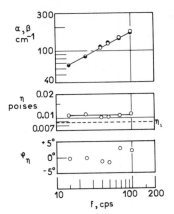

FIG. 10 Measured frequency dependence of β, α, η, and φ_η for 0.3% Baymal in water at 25°C.

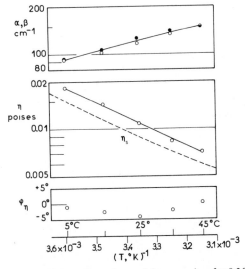

FIG. 11 Measured temperature dependence of β, α, η, and φ_η for 0.3% Baymal in water at 50 cps.

Measurements were made for 0.3% Baymal in a modified aqueous environment. The environment was modified by the addition of 0.5% of the water soluble polymer, polyethylene oxide having a molecular weight of 4×10^6. It may be anticipated that this addition will have more influence than simply increasing the value of the solvent viscosity, for the polymer itself exhibits viscoelastic behavior at low frequencies.

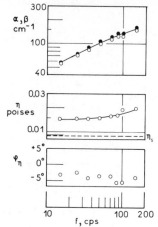

FIG. 12   Measured frequency dependence of β, α, η, and φ_η for 0.3% Baymal plus 0.5% polyethylene oxide in water at 25°C.

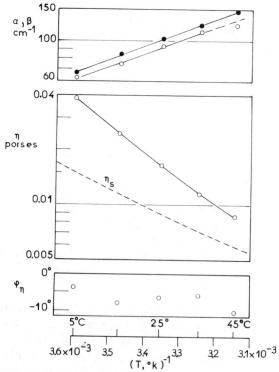

FIG. 13   Measured temperature dependence of β, α, η, and φ_η for 0.3% Baymal plus 0.5% polyethylene oxide in water at 50 cps.

Figure 12 shows the frequency dependence. It is seen that there is an indication of unusual behavior in that the magnitude of the viscosity, η, increases slightly with frequency while the normal behavior is to decrease. Figure 13 shows the temperature effect which is more pronounced than for the pure water, but otherwise appears normal. These measurements were made to explore the possibility of study of the viscous environment of small particles in the presence of long chain macromolecules. Comparison measurements have also been carried out in glycerol solutions, the indications being that a perfectly normal viscous environment is maintained.

6. Conclusion

From the results of measurement carried out using a low concentration of Baymal in water, it is seen that the experimental apparatus described will adequately yield shear wave propagation curves for liquids of low viscosity and low rigidity. The results of these measurements are consistent with the mechanical model for a dilute suspension of rigid ellipsoidal macromolecules. It is also concluded that at very low concentrations Baymal is a good material for producing an optically birefringent medium while making a negligible contribution to its mechanical properties. In this way one may obtain an aqueous, essentially purely viscous, birefringent liquid in which the mechanical properties of certain nonbirefringent additives may be studied.

REFERENCES

1. J. D. Ferry and F. E. Helders, *Biochim. Biophys. Acta* **23**, 569 (1957).
2. F. E. Helders, J. D. Ferry, H. Markovitz, and L. J. Fapas, *J. Phys. Chem.* **60**, 1575 (1956).
3. G. B. Thurston and J. L. Schrag, *J. Appl. Phys.* **35**, 144 (1964).
4. J. Bugosh, R. L. Brown, J. R. McWhorter, G. W. Sears, and R. J. Sippel, *Ind. Engr. Chem. Prod. Res. Develop.* **1**, 157 (1962).
5. J. Bugosh, *J. Phys. Chem.* **65**, 1709 (1961).
6. R. Cerf, *J. Phys. Radium* **13**, 458 (1952).
7. A. Peterlin and H. A. Stuart, *Z. Physik* **112**, 1 (1939).
8. R. Cerf and G. B. Thurston, *J. Chim. Phys.* **61**, 1457 (1964).

The Critical Wall Shear Stress for Reduction of Turbulent Drag in Pipe Flow†

P. S. VIRK, E. W. MERRILL, H. S. MICKLEY,
and K. A. SMITH

Department of Chemical Engineering
Massachusetts Institute of Technology
Cambridge, Massachusetts

Analysis of pipe flow data obtained by several investigators of the Toms phenomenon in the turbulent flow of dilute polymer solutions indicates one striking trend: namely, that the onset of drag reduction occurs only after the wall shear stress exceeds a "critical" value, characteristic of the macromolecule in solution. Motivated by this the following hypothesis is proposed: the onset of drag reduction occurs at a constant value of the product $D_M k_d^*$, which is a ratio of the dimensions of the macromolecule in solution (D_M) and the dissipation wavenumber (k_d^*) characteristic of the turbulent flow.

Using twice the rms radius of gyration of the macromolecule for D_M and $(u_\tau^*/v) = (\tau_w^*/\rho)^{1/2}/v$ as a scale for k_d^*, the data of several investigators—and new data for polyethylene oxide polymers obtained in our laboratory—appear to bear out the consequences of the above hypothesis, viz:

(1) The value of $(\tau_w^*)^{1/2}$—the wall shear stress at the onset of drag reduction—should be independent of pipe size for a given macromolecule.

(2) For the same pipe, $(\tau_w^*)^{1/2}$ should vary inversely as the rms radius of gyration of the macromolecule.

(3) For a given pipe size-macromolecule combination, $(\tau_w^*)^{1/2}$ should be independent of concentration.

(4) The value of $D_M k_d^*$ should be constant in all cases.

Sufficient data to verify postulate (4) are not at present available. The best value for $D_M k_d^*$—obtained from data on polyethylene oxides in water—is about 0.0025.

† This work was carried out under Contract Nonr-3963(10) from the Office of Naval Research.

1. Introduction

The Toms phenomenon concerns the reduction of drag in a turbulent shear flow by the addition of small quantities of soluble macromolecules to the micromolecular solvent. It is best illustrated by a hydraulic diagram such as Fig. 1, which is a plot of the original data of Toms,[1] for solutions of polymethylmethacrylate in monochlorobenzene. The significant outcome of the Toms phenomenon is that the *specific power* required to sustain a turbulent flow is decreased—resulting either in higher flow rates for the same power consumption (i.e., pressure gradient) or lower power consumption for the same flow rate.

2. Previous Investigations

Since Toms (1948), several workers have investigated the phenomenon.[2-6,14] The variety of pipe sizes and macromolecule-solvent combinations used is illustrated in Fig. 2, which is a summary of the data to date and indicates the flow regions of the above investigators. Several explanations have been offered for the Toms phenomenon[2,7] but will not be discussed because all of them are somewhat speculative. This paper focuses solely on one interesting experimental observation.

3. The Onset of Drag Reduction

All the data taken are qualitatively similar to those of Toms (Fig. 1) and all of them exhibit one striking trend. Namely, that for a given macromolecule-solvent-pipe combination, the onset of drag reduction occurs only after a certain value of the wall shear stress has been exceeded, regardless of the concentration of polymer provided, of course, that the solution is dilute in the thermodynamic sense.[15] This "critical" or "onset" wall shear stress does depend on the molecular weight of the polymer but appears quite independent of the pipe diameter if the macromolecule-solvent pair remains the same.

The above suggests that a necessary condition exists which explicitly connects the macromolecule causing the Toms phenomenon and the turbulent shear flow in question. Only when this condition is satisfied is it possible for a macromolecular solution to exhibit drag reduction. It appears reasonable to assume that the onset of drag reduction would be ascertained by parameters characteristic of

  (i)   the turbulence pertaining in the flow;
  (ii) the macromolecule causing drag reduction.

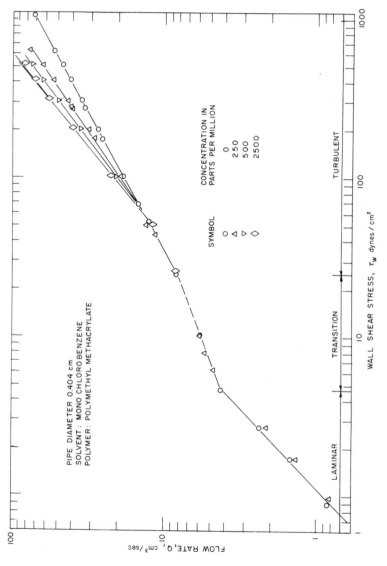

FIG. 1   Data of Toms.[1]

(i) The structure of turbulence in a turbulent pipe flow is not yet well understood and, therefore, it is difficult to choose an entirely satisfactory turbulent scale. However, since drag reduction is an "energetic" type of phenomenon and it is quite well known that the energy action

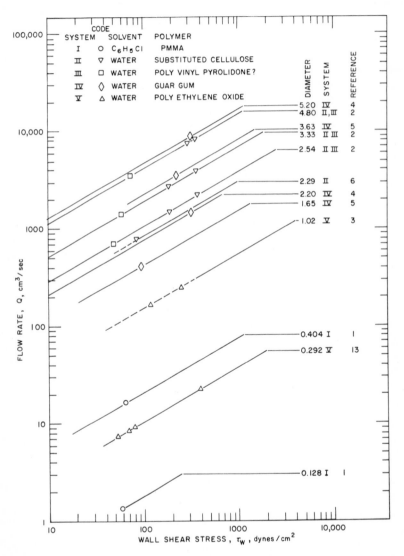

Fig. 2 Summary of data indicating polymer-solvent systems studied and flow regions covered.

in a pipe flow occurs very close to the wall,[8,9] the parameter chosen to characterize the turbulence was a wavenumber, k_d, derived from the turbulent energy spectrum close to the wall. k_d was defined as the wave-number where the dissipation is a maximum, i.e., the quantity $k^2 E(k)$ is a maximum. This definition of k_d is reminiscent of, but different from, the so called "microscale" of the turbulent flow.

(ii) The macromolecule was characterized by a "Diameter," $D_M = 2R_G$, derived from it rms radius of gyration after the method of Tanford.[10] This is valid only for dilute solutions where interactions between neighboring macromolecules are negligibly small.

4. The Onset of Drag Reduction Hypothesis

With the background above, the following hypothesis was formulated: The onset of drag reduction in the turbulent flow of dilute polymer solutions occurs at a constant value of the product $D_M k_d^*$ which is a ratio of the dimensions of the macromolecule and the fine scale of the turbulent shear flow.

To test this hypothesis it is necessary to devise rules for scaling k_d^* when actual measurements of the turbulent energy spectrum do not exist. It can be shown (Appendix) that if the Reynolds number is high enough, then

$$k_d^* = A u_\tau^*/\nu = A(\tau_w^*/\rho)^{1/2}/\nu \qquad (4.1)$$

where A is a constant that depends only on the position (y^+) in the pipe.

The mathematical form of the hypothesis is

$$D_M k_d^* = C \qquad (4.2)$$

where C is a universal constant and the asterisk (*) indicates values taken at the "critical" or "onset" point for drag reduction. If (4.1) is substituted into (4.2) one gets

$$D_M(\tau_w^*/\rho)^{1/2}/\nu = C/A = C' \qquad (4.3)$$

or

$$(\tau_w^*)^{1/2} = C''/R_G \qquad (C'' = C\nu\rho^{1/2}/2A) \qquad (4.4)$$

Equation (4.4) is the most convenient form of the hypothesis for a given solvent-polymer family.

The hypothesis (4.2) has the following ramifications which provide means of testing its validity:

(1) The value of $(\tau_w^*)^{1/2}$—the wall shear stress at the onset of drag reduction—should be independent of pipe diameter for a given macro-molecule.

(2) For the same pipe, $(\tau_w{}^*)^{1/2}$ should vary inversely as the rms radius of gyration of the macromolecule.

(3) For a given pipe-macromolecule combination, $(\tau_w{}^*)^{1/2}$ should be independent of the concentration of polymer.

(4) The value of the dimensionless onset group, $(D_M k_d{}^*)$, should be a constant in all cases.

These consequences can be tested with data quoted previously and appear to be satisfied. However, none of the investigators, except Fabula,[3] and Toms,[1] characterized their polymers carefully; Fabula,[3] did not get data at the onset point itself so that, on the whole, prior work did not provide conclusive evidence. The purpose of the investigation described below was to carry out definitive experiments to test the hypothesis quoted above. To do this it was decided to use 4 molecular weights of a homologous series of polymers in a single solvent and 2 widely different pipe diameters. The polymers used were polyethylene oxides, the solvent, water, and the 2 pipe diameters about 0.3 and 3.0 cm, respectively. Only the experiments in the 0.3 cm diameter pipe are reported below.

5. Experimental Materials and Apparatus

The polymers were obtained from Union Carbide Company, which markets them as Polyox water soluble resins. They were used as received. Various concentrations of polymer for the experimental runs were got by suitably diluting concentrated master batches. The intrinsic viscosity of each master batch was measured before and after each series of runs using the low shear GDM viscometer.[11]

A photograph of the experimental apparatus is shown in Fig. 3. It consists of a blowdown tank from which liquid is forced, under a constant gas (nitrogen) pressure, for one pass through a precision bore stainless steel tube about 250 diameters long. The tube has 4 pressure taps, one every 35 diameters, beginning 120 diameters from the entrance. The pressure differential between any two taps was read by a transducer, accurate to a little better than 1 % of the absolute value over most of the range. The volumetric flow rate was measured directly with a "bucket and stop-watch" arrangement using a microswitch, an electric timer, and a graduated cylinder. The accuracy of the flow rate measurement was about $\frac{1}{2}\%$.

6. Data

The system was calibrated by running distilled water through it. The results agreed closely with the well established values for smooth tubes.

FIG. 3   Experimental apparatus.

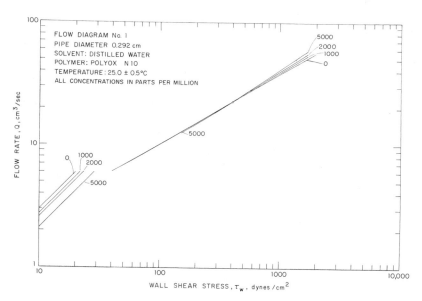

FIG. 4   Flow diagram 1, Polyox N10 in distilled water.

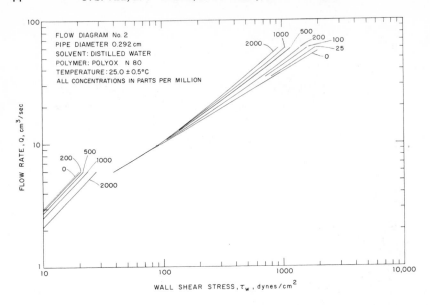

FIG. 5   Flow Diagram 2, Polyox N80 in distilled water.

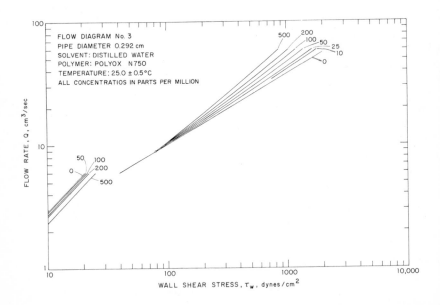

FIG. 6   Flow Diagram 3, Polyox N750 in distilled water.

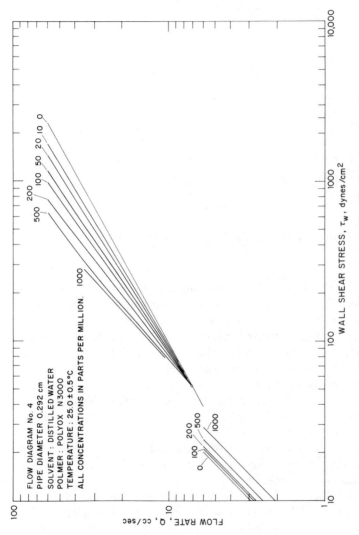

FIG. 7 Flow Diagram 4, Polyox N3000 in distilled water.

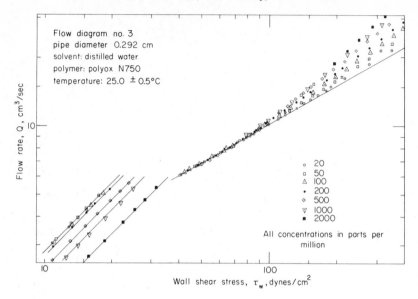

FIG. 8   Flow Diagram 3, Polyox N750 in distilled water, expanded around the critical wall shear stress.

An error analysis of the water data showed that for the entire experimental range, the 99% confidence belt for the wall shear stress (at a given flow rate) was always better than 1% of the absolute value.

Figures 4–7 present the data for the 4 Polyox polymers tested. They are qualitatively very similar and all of them exhibit the "onset" phenomenon quite clearly. Note also that they are quite similar to the data of Toms shown earlier in Fig. 1. Figure 8 is a detail of the flow in the region of the critical wall shear stress for Polyox N750 having a molecular weight of about 580,000. It illustrates the 4 regions encountered in a flow of this nature:

(1) Laminar flow where the 45° lines indicate Newtonian behavior. It is interesting to note that in all the cases, the intrinsic viscosities got from this laminar regime at the relatively high shear rates prevalent (about $1000 \, \text{sec}^{-1}$) checked well with the intrinsic viscosities got from the low shear GDM viscometer for the corresponding master batches. This indicates that the solutions used had no shear-thinning tendencies and were not pseudoplastic.

(2) The transition region between laminar and turbulent flow. This appears as a blank in the figure because no stable readings could be got in this region.

(3) The turbulent regime in which the polymer solutions follow lines parallel to the pure solvent. The lines for various concentrations come much closer together in the turbulent region because of the greatly reduced dependence on the viscosity (from a 1.0 power law in laminar to a 0.23 power law in turbulent flow). Note that in this region there is no drag reduction—in fact the drag is slightly increased, corresponding to the increased viscosity of the polymer solutions.

(4) The region of drag reduction that is characteristic of the Toms phenomenon. Throughout this region the specific power consumption is lower than for the pure solvent.

Figure 8 illustrates that the division between regions (3) and (4) is quite sharp and the critical wall shear stress that separates them quite constant over a 100-fold range of concentration.

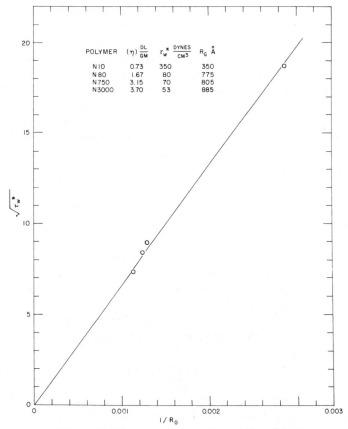

POLYMER	$(\eta) \frac{DL}{GM}$	$\tau_w^* \frac{DYNES}{CM^3}$	$R_G \ \mathring{A}$
N 10	0.73	350	350
N 80	1.67	80	775
N 750	3.15	70	805
N 3000	3.70	53	885

FIG. 9   Summary of Polyox results, $(\tau_w^*)^{1/2}$ vs $(1/R_G)$.

7. Discussion of Results

The 4 consequences of the onset of drag reduction hypothesis will now be discussed in the order listed earlier:

(1) Since the pipe diameter was not varied in the data just presented, no conclusions can be drawn in this regard. However, data of several workers,[1,2,4] listed in Table I (described later) show that for a given macromolecule, the value of $(u_\tau{}^*/v)$ is quite independent of the pipe diameter used.

(2) Figure 9 is a tabulation of the intrinsic viscosities, the rms radii of gyration (experimentally determined from light-scattering data of Shin,[13]) and the critical wall shear stresses for the polymers studied. Also, $(\tau_w{}^*)^{1/2}$ is plotted against $(1/R_G)$. As predicted, the result of the plot is a straight line through the origin.

(3) As was shown by the data (Figs. 4–8) the critical wall shear stress is quite independent of the concentration.

(4) It would be very interesting to know if the onset group $(D_M k_d{}^*)$ is indeed a constant for all polymer-solvent systems, and if this is so, what the absolute value is. To do this we need

(i) An accurate way of determining the absolute value of $k_d{}^*$ for a pipe flow. This implies a much better knowledge of the structure of turbulent pipe flow than is currently possessed.

(ii) Thorough characterization of the macromolecule used in the solvent—especially its conformation in dilute solutions and its response to high mean shear rates.

(iii) Considerably more data than is currently available.

Table I is a summary of all the data obtained to date. Values of R_G have been obtained from light-scattering data (e.g., Shin[13]) where possible because this is the most direct. Elsewhere, they have been estimated from either the intrinsic viscosity or the molecular weight of the polymer in question using the recommendations of Kurata and Stockmeyer.[12] In the case of natural gums (like Guar gum) the estimates are extremely uncertain. Values of $k_d{}^*$ have been estimated from the critical wall shear stresses using the data of Laufer[8] and the scaling rules derived in Appendix. Since the constant, A, in (4.1) depends on position in the pipe, values have been taken for $y^+ = 10$.

All the values of $(D_M k_d{}^*)$ fall between 0.0015 and 0.0045, which establishes an order of magnitude for the onset constant. It is noteworthy, however, that for the two cases where the polymers were closely characterized,[1,14] and, therefore, permitted an accurate estimate of R_G, the values are very close to 0.0025 and constant. The extremes are provided

TABLE I

SUMMARY OF CRITICAL WALL SHEAR STRESS DATA

System	Polymer*-solvent† system^a	$[\eta]$ (dl/gm)	Diameter (cm)	R_G (Å)	$(u_\tau^*/v)^b$ (cm^{-1})	$D_M k_d^*$ $= 2R_G(0.2u_\tau^*/v)^c$	Ref.
I	PMMA*	3.90	0.128	600	1030	0.00248	1
	MCB†	3.90	0.404	600	1100	0.00264	1
II	CMC* Water†	10	2.29	500	950	0.00190	6
		—	2.54	—	1930	—	2
	?*	—	3.33	—	1890	—	2
	Water†	—	4.80	—	1880	—	2
		—	2.54	—	1370	—	2
	?*	—	3.33	—	1370	—	2
	Water†	—	4.80	—	1730	—	2
III		—	2.54	—	710	—	2
	PVP?*	—	3.33	—	770	—	2
	Water†	—	4.80	—	870	—	2
IV	Guar gum*	7.0	2.20	200	1800	0.00144	4
	Water†	7.0	5.02	200	1780	0.00143	4
		19.0	1.65	400	980	0.00157	5
		19.0	3.63	400	1330	0.00212	5
V	Peo*	2.7	1.02	740	1580	0.00469	3
	Water†	4.3	1.02	960	1100	0.00425	3
		0.73	0.292	350	1870	0.00262	14
		1.67	0.292	775	890	0.00274	14
		3.15	0.292	805	835	0.00269	14
		3.70	0.292	885	730	0.00259	14

^{a} Abbreviations used for polymer-solvent systems:

   MCB   Monochlorobenzene
   PMMA   Poly(methylmethacrylate)
   CMC   Sodium carboxymethylcellulose
   PVP   Poly(vinyl pyrolidone)
   PEO   Poly (ethylene oxide)
   ?   Indicates uncertainty about the polymer used.
^{b} v for water around 0.01.
^{c} Recommended value for the onset constant, $(D_M k_d^*)$: 0.0025.

by investigations using Guar gum, which is a natural polymer and very difficult to characterize, and by the data of Fabula,[3] which involved extrapolation of the flow curves back to the critical wall shear stress. Because the slopes of the curves for dilute polymer solutions are quite close to that of the pure solvent, the error involved in the extrapolation is quite high. In summary, regarding the value of the onset constant, the most that can be said at present is that the order of magnitude has been established and that the best value appears to be 0.0025.

From all of the foregoing it may be said that the onset of drag reduction hypothesis made in Section 4 appears to be valid in the light of present experimental evidence.

The significance of the ratio between the macromolecular size and the fine scale of the turbulence is as yet uncertain—limited by our ignorance of both the turbulent mechanism and the behavior of macromolecules in a shear flow. The small values of the onset constant could, for example, point to

(a)   an extension of the macromolecule to many times its zero-shear random coiling size (which is what the rms radius of gyration is) or,

(b)   a strong nonlinear interaction between wavenumbers far removed from each other (by as much as, say, a factor of 10^3), but final conclusions cannot be drawn at present.

One interesting application of the onset constant is to establish the regions in which a given macromolecule will exhibit the Toms phenomenon, given, of course, information on the macromolecule being used. Using the best value of 0.0025 for C, and making the necessary conversions, the relevant form of (4.4) becomes

$$\tau_w{}^* = \rho(0.625 \times 10^6 \nu/R_G)^2 \tag{7.1}$$

Note that (7.1) is a dimensional equation and the units must be as given in the nomenclature section. To get drag reduction, the value of the wall shear stress must exceed $\tau_w{}^*$ calculated in Eq. (7.1).

8. Summary

A hypothesis is presented regarding the onset of drag reduction in the turbulent flow of dilute polymer solutions. Presented also is some new data for the polyethylene oxide water system which, together with previous data, appear to confirm the consequences of the hypothesis. The hypothesis permits the establishment of criteria which predict whether—or not—a given polymer will be capable of reducing drag in a turbulent pipe flow.

Appendix: Scaling Rules for the Dissipation Wavenumber, k_d

1. THE UNIVERSAL EQUILIBRIUM

The dissipation wavenumber k_d is defined as the wavenumber where the maximum dissipation occurs—that is the value of the second moment about the origin, $k^2 E(k)$, is a maximum. This definition of k_d heavily weights the regions of the turbulent energy spectrum which contribute most to the dissipation of the turbulent energy. It is well known that when the Reynolds number is high enough, then, beyond a certain wavenumber, the so-called universal equilibrium exists.[9] In this region of the spectrum the controlling parameters are

(1) The dissipation, ε cm^2/sec^3
(2) The kinematic viscosity, ν cm^2/sec

and the energy spectrum becomes universal when normalized with respect to these two. The above applies, strictly speaking, only for an isotropic turbulence.

2. PIPE FLOW TURBULENCE[8]

In a pipe flow the turbulence is anisotropic, but it is quite reasonable to assume that the high end of the spectrum—the region relevant to k_d —is isotropic to a first approximation. Also at any point in the pipe,

dissipation of turbulence energy $\cong$ production of turbulence energy

and .

$$\text{production} = f(y^+) \text{ only when normalized by } (u_\tau{}^4/\nu)$$

Thus,

$$\text{dissipation} = \text{production} = B(u_\tau{}^4/\nu)$$

where B is a constant characteristic of the position (i.e., y^+) only.

3. THE SCALING RULES

In the universal equilibrium range, the length scale is derived from the two controlling parameters and is

$$L = (\nu^3/\varepsilon)^{1/4} = (1/a)(\nu/u_\tau) \qquad \text{where} \quad a = B^{1/4}$$

Using this scale, and a corresponding time scale given by

$$T = (1/b)(\nu/u_\tau{}^2) \qquad \text{where} \quad b = B^{1/2}$$

one can derive the values of the universal spectrum, given, of course, one experimental spectrum with known parameters. For this latter, the results of Laufer,[8] were used. From the universal spectrum, one can compute the values of $K^2E(K)$ and thence arrive at a value for K_d, a dimensionless, universal dissipation wavenumber. Once K_d is known we can reverse the process for any other flow, provided, of course, that the relevant parameters (v and u_τ) are known. The relevant formula is

$$k_d = K_d a u_\tau/v = A u_\tau/v$$

The value of A, derived from Laufer's data, is about 0.20 for a y^+ of 10.

NOMENCLATURE

A	Spectrum scaling constant, $\simeq 0.2$ at $y^+ = 10$	k_d	Dissipation wavenumber, cm^{-1}
C	Onset of drag reduction constant, dimensionless	R_G	rms radius of gyration of macromolecule, Å
C'	Constant	u_τ	Friction velocity, cm/sec
C''	Constant	τ_w	Wall shear stress, dynes/cm^2
D_M	Macromolecule diameter, Å	v	Kinematic viscosity, cm^2/sec
$E(k)$	Fraction of turbulent energy associated with wavenumber k, cm^3/sec^2	ρ	Solvent density, gm/cm^3
k	Wavenumber, cm^{-1}	$[\eta]$	Intrinsic viscosity, dl/gm
		$*$	Superscript indicates values taken at the point of onset of drag reduction

REFERENCES

1. B. A. Toms, *Proc. 1st Intern. Congr. on Rheology 1948*, Vol. II, p. 135. North-Holland Publ., Amsterdam, 1948.
2. J. G. Savins, A.I.Ch.E. *Symp. on Non-Newtonian Fluid Mech.*, 56th Annual meeting, Houston, 1963.
3. A. G. Fabula, Paper 199, *4th Intern. Congr. on Rheology, Brown University, Providence, Rhode Island*, 1963.
4. C. Elata and J. Tirosh, Informal Report to the O.N.R. Contract No. 62558-4093 (1965).
5. C. S. Wells, Preprint 64-36, *AIAA Meeting*, New York (1964).
6. J. F. Ripken and M. Pilch, St. Anthony Falls Hydraulic Lab., Univ. of Minnesota, Paper 42 (1963).
7. J. G. Oldroyd, *Proc. 1st Intern. Congr. on Rheology, 1948*, Vol. II, p. 130. North-Holland Publ. Amsterdam, 1948.
8. J. Laufer, NACA, Report 1174 (1954).
9. J. O. Hinze, "Turbulence." McGraw-Hill, New York, 1958.
10. C. Tanford, "The Physical Chemistry of Macromolecules." Wiley, New York, 1961.
11. P. J. Gilinson, C. R. Dauwalter, and E. W. Merrill, *Trans. Soc. Rheology*, 7, 303 (1963).
12. M. Kurata and W. H. Stockmeyer, *Fortschr. Hochpolym. Forsch.* 3, 192 (1963).
13. H. Shin, Sc.D. Thesis, Chemical Engineering Dept., MIT, 1965.
14. P. S. Virk, Sc.D. Thesis, Chemical Engineering Dept., MIT, 1966.
15. P. J. Flory, "Principles of Polymer Chemistry." Cornell Univ. Press, Ithaca, New York, 1953.

Properties of a Class of Constitutive Equations Stated in a Nontrivial Implicit Form†

A. J. A. MORGAN

Department of Engineering
University of California
Los Angeles, California

1. Introduction

In brief outline, we present some results obtained in a preliminary study of a correctly set‡ class of constitutive equations whose main distinguishing characteristic is that they are originally given in an easily motivated nontrivial implicit form. Some features of these results may be of interest and reveal other possibilities for further investigation.

Our aim is to determine if the properties of these equations are such that they can be used to construct characteristic surfaces in the principal-stress space. We look for a possible connection between these surfaces and the yield surfaces used in plasticity theory.

Once the starting point is obtained, the remainder of the investigation is purely algebraic in nature. In fact, we shall be concerned with determining the properties of the solutions of a set of six simultaneous quadratic equations.

Although not essential, we here (see also Morgan[1]) restrict our remarks to materials whose constitutive equations are stated in terms of a dimensionless stress tensor $\mathbf{T}$ and the left Cauchy–Green deformation tensor $\mathbf{B}$ $(=\mathbf{V}^2 = \mathbf{F}\mathbf{F}^T)$.§ We employ a rectangular Cartesian coordinate system.

Our starting point is generated by three observations:

1. One form of the classical constitutive equations on which isotropic finite elasticity theory is based (Truesdell and Noll,[3] §47) may be

---

† This presentation summarizes that given in Morgan.[1]

‡ I.e., satisfying the requisite invariance principles given in Noll,[2] §11, Truesdell and Noll,[3] §19, and Morgan,[4] §9: material objectivity (or, constitutive invariance) and dimensional homogeneity.

§ We adhere to the notation used in Truesdell and Noll.[3] For pertinent definitions see Noll[2] and Truesdell and Noll,[3] §§21, 23.

written as

$$\mathbf{T} = \mathbf{f}(\mathbf{B}) = \varphi_0\mathbf{I} + \varphi_1\mathbf{B} + \varphi_2\mathbf{B}^2. \tag{1}$$

This relation is a special case of an equation of the form:

$$\mathfrak{F}(\mathbf{T}, \mathbf{B}) = \mathbf{0}, \tag{2}$$

which, when $\mathfrak{F}$ is isotropic, satisfies the principles of material objectivity and dimensional invariance.[2-4] Whenever $\mathfrak{F}$ has a form more general than that obtaining in the classical case, Eq. (2) should serve to represent a wider range of phenomena.

2. In general, under Eq. (2), the principal axes of $\mathbf{T}$ and $\mathbf{B}$ need not be coincident. In contrast such is always the case with Eq. (1).

3. If in cases more general than (1), Eq. (2) can be inverted for the components of $\mathbf{T}$ in terms of those of $\mathbf{B}$, then several solution branches may be obtained, as conjectured in Morgan.[4]

It is this third observation which brings to the forefront the possibility that some type of characteristic surface in the principal-stress space may emerge as a property of some (nontrivially invertible for $\mathbf{T}$) forms of Eq. (2).

2. Formulation

As we have already indicated, when $\mathfrak{F}$ is isotropic and $\mathbf{T}$ is dimensionless, the constitutive equation†

$$\mathfrak{F}(\mathbf{T}, \mathbf{B}) = \mathbf{0} \tag{2}$$

satisfies the principles of material objectivity and dimensionless invariance. Furthermore, under these conditions, since $\mathbf{T}$ and $\mathbf{B}$ are symmetric, on invoking a result due to Rivlin and Ericksen[5] we can at once assert that Eq. (2) has the representation:

$$\mathbf{T} + (\alpha\mathbf{B} + \beta\mathbf{B}^2)\mathbf{T} + \mathbf{T}(\alpha\mathbf{B} + \beta\mathbf{B}^2) + (\tfrac{1}{2}\gamma\mathbf{I} + \delta\mathbf{B} + \varepsilon\mathbf{B}^2)\mathbf{T}^2$$
$$+ \mathbf{T}^2(\tfrac{1}{2}\gamma\mathbf{I} + \delta\mathbf{B} + \varepsilon\mathbf{B}^2) = \psi_0\mathbf{I} + \psi_1\mathbf{B} + \psi_2\mathbf{B}^2, \tag{3}$$

where the scalar coefficients are, in general, the values of functions of the ten basic scalar-valued invariants:

$$\operatorname{tr}\mathbf{B}, \quad \operatorname{tr}\mathbf{B}^2, \quad \operatorname{tr}\mathbf{B}^3, \quad \operatorname{tr}\mathbf{T}, \quad \operatorname{tr}\mathbf{T}^2, \quad \operatorname{tr}\mathbf{T}^3, \quad \operatorname{tr}\mathbf{BT}, \quad \operatorname{tr}\mathbf{BT}^2,$$
$$\operatorname{tr}\mathbf{B}^2\mathbf{T}, \quad \operatorname{tr}\mathbf{B}^2\mathbf{T}^2. \tag{4}$$

However, Eq. (3) cannot be inverted for the components of $\mathbf{T}$ in terms of those of $\mathbf{B}$ unless some additional assumption is introduced. So as to obtain a direct reduction to nonlinear elasticity theory we employ a

† Which defines a class of (say) "hypso-elastic" materials, including "elastic" materials as a special case.

simpler form for $\mathfrak{F}$, supposing that† all the response functions are dependent only on the three principal invariants of **B**, i.e.,

$$\alpha, \ldots, \gamma, \quad \psi_0, \quad \psi_1, \quad \psi_2 = \hat{\alpha}, \ldots, \hat{\gamma}, \quad \hat{\psi}_0, \quad \hat{\psi}_1, \quad \hat{\psi}_2(I_B, II_B, III_B). \quad (5)$$

This assumption does not destroy the main features of Eq. (3) which we wish to preserve: (1) noncoincidence of the principal axes of **T** and **B**, and (2) the existence of a multiplicity of solution branches. Furthermore, since **B** is symmetric it can always be diagonalized by an orthogonal transformation; hence, without any further loss of generality, we may take **B** to be given in diagonal form. Writing Eq. (3) in the form:

$$\mathbf{T} + \mathbb{C}\mathbf{T} + \mathbf{T}\mathbb{C} + \mathfrak{D}\mathbf{T}^2 + \mathbf{T}^2\mathfrak{D} = \mathbb{E} \quad (6)$$

we shall also suppose that

$$\lim_{\mathbf{B} \to \mathbf{I}} \hat{\mathbb{C}}(\mathbf{B}) = 0, \qquad \lim_{\mathbf{B} \to \mathbf{I}} \hat{\mathfrak{D}}(\mathbf{B}) = \tfrac{1}{2}\gamma_0 \mathbf{I}, \qquad \lim_{\mathbf{B} \to \mathbf{I}} \hat{\mathbb{E}}(\mathbf{B}) = 0, \quad (7)$$

where $\hat{\mathbb{C}}$, $\hat{\mathfrak{D}}$, and $\hat{\mathbb{E}}$ are the functions whose values are $\mathbb{C}$, $\mathfrak{D}$, and $\mathbb{E}$, respectively, and

$$\gamma_0 = \hat{\gamma}(3, 3, 1).$$

These assumptions as to the behavior of the coefficient tensors are introduced so that, at zero deformation, $(7)_1$ discards the effect of the linear terms in (6) which do not introduce significant differences in comparison with the classical theories, $(7)_2$ serves to retain the essential nonlinear effect of the $\mathbf{T}^2$ terms in their simplest form, and $(7)_3$ duplicates the behavior of $\hat{\mathbb{E}}$ in nonlinear elasticity theory.

3. Reduction to Component Form

After some manipulation, Eq. (6) can be written as a set of six simultaneous quadratic equations:

$$t_{11}^2 + t_{12}^2 + t_{13}^2 + 2f_1 t_{11} = g_1,$$

$$t_{12}^2 + t_{22}^2 + t_{23}^2 + 2f_2 t_{22} = g_2,$$

$$t_{13}^2 + t_{23}^2 + t_{33}^2 + 2f_3 t_{33} = g_3,$$

$$t_{11}t_{12} + t_{12}t_{22} + t_{13}t_{23} + f_{12}t_{12} = 0,$$

$$t_{11}t_{13} + t_{12}t_{23} + t_{13}t_{33} + f_{13}t_{13} = 0,$$

$$t_{12}t_{13} + t_{22}t_{23} + t_{23}t_{33} + f_{23}t_{23} = 0,$$

$$(8)$$

† This motivates our study of the class of constitutive equations defined by Eqs. (3) and (5); they serve to define a class of ideal materials or, once the response functions are specified, a particular (say, "hypstre-elastic") material. Motivation aside, the study of hypstre-elastic materials is of intrinsic interest.

where in terms of the values of the original response functions and the principal components B_Δ of $\mathbf{B}$ ($\Delta, \Gamma = 1, 2, 3$):

$$f_\Delta = \frac{1 + 2(\alpha B_\Delta + \beta B_\Delta{}^2)}{2\gamma + \delta B_\Delta + \varepsilon B_\Delta{}^2},$$

$$f_{\Delta\Gamma} = \frac{1 + \alpha(B_\Delta + B_\Gamma) + \beta(B_\Delta{}^2 + B_\Gamma{}^2)}{\gamma + \delta(B_\Delta + B_\Gamma) + \varepsilon(B_\Delta{}^2 + B_\Gamma{}^2)}, \tag{9}$$

$$g_\Delta = \frac{\psi_0 + \psi_1 B_\Delta + \psi_2 B_\Delta{}^2}{\gamma + \delta B_\Delta + \varepsilon B_\Delta{}^2}.$$

Our task is to obtain solutions of these six simultaneous quadratic equations. We separately consider two types of solutions. One, where the principal axes of $\mathbf{T}$ and $\mathbf{B}$ are coincident (i.e., $t_{12} = t_{13} = t_{23} = 0$)— we call these *diagonal*. When this property does not hold, then we call the solutions *nondiagonal*.

TABLE I

ORDERING OF THE DIAGONAL-SOLUTION BRANCHES[a]

BRANCH NO.	CHOICE OF SIGN FOR t_{11}	t_{22}	t_{33}	$t_{11}^{(1)}$	$t_{22}^{(1)}$	$t_{33}^{(1)}$
1	+	+	+	0	0	0
2	−	+	+	$-\dfrac{1}{\gamma_0}$	0	0
3	+	−	+	0	$-\dfrac{1}{\gamma_0}$	0
4	+	+	−	0	0	$-\dfrac{1}{\gamma_0}$
5	+	−	−	0	$-\dfrac{1}{\gamma_0}$	$-\dfrac{1}{\gamma_0}$
6	−	+	−	$-\dfrac{1}{\gamma_0}$	0	$-\dfrac{1}{\gamma_0}$
7	−	−	+	$-\dfrac{1}{\gamma_0}$	$-\dfrac{1}{\gamma_0}$	0
8	−	−	−	$-\dfrac{1}{\gamma_0}$	$-\dfrac{1}{\gamma_0}$	$-\dfrac{1}{\gamma_0}$

[a] From Morgan.[1]

A. DIAGONAL SOLUTIONS

In this case we immediately find

$$t_{\Delta\Delta} = -f_\Delta \pm \sqrt{f_\Delta{}^2 + g_\Delta} \equiv -f_\Delta \pm \sqrt{D_\Delta}, \qquad \Delta = 1, 2, 3. \tag{10}$$

Since the plus or minus signs in (10) can be independently chosen, our solution has a total of *eight* branches.

On invoking our assumption (7) we find that each of these eight branches corresponds to an initial state of stress as shown in Table I. Note that only for branch 1 does zero stress correspond to zero deformation. For branch 8 we obtain a spherical state of stress at zero deformation.

B. NONDIAGONAL SOLUTIONS

Solving the last three of Eqs. (8) for the shear components in terms of the normal components of **T** we obtain the four branches:

$$t_{12} = \begin{Bmatrix} + \\ + \\ - \\ - \end{Bmatrix} \{[f_{13} + t_{11} + t_{33}][f_{23} + t_{22} + t_{33}]\}^{1/2},$$

$$t_{13} = \begin{Bmatrix} + \\ - \\ + \\ - \end{Bmatrix} \{[f_{12} + t_{11} + t_{22}][f_{23} + t_{22} + t_{33}]\}^{1/2}, \tag{11}$$

$$t_{23} = \begin{Bmatrix} - \\ + \\ + \\ - \end{Bmatrix} \{[f_{12} + t_{11} + t_{22}][f_{13} + t_{11} + t_{33}]\}^{1/2}.$$

Using these, we can after some manipulation place the first three of Eqs. (8) in the form:

$$A_1(t_{22} + t_{33}) + \bar{B}_1 = (t_{11} + t_{22} + t_{33} + C_1)^2,$$
$$A_2(t_{11} + t_{33}) + \bar{B}_2 = (t_{11} + t_{22} + t_{33} + C_2)^2, \tag{12}$$
$$A_3(t_{11} + t_{22}) + \bar{B}_3 = (t_{11} + t_{22} + t_{33} + C_3)^2,$$

where the A's, $\bar{B}$'s, and C's are combinations of the f_Δ, $f_{\Delta\Gamma}$, and g_Δ whose particular form need not concern us here; however, see Morgan.[1]

We may, equivalently, write Eqs. (12) as

$$A_1 t_{11} - A_3 t_{33} = E_{13}, \qquad A_2 t_{22} - A_3 t_{33} = E_{23},$$

$$A_3(t_{11} + t_{22}) + \bar{B}_3 = (t_{11} + t_{22} + t_{33} + C_3)^2. \tag{13}$$

4. Properties of the Nondiagonal Solutions

The formal solutions of Eqs. (13) are easily obtained (Morgan[1]). We do not present the results here since they are not too illuminating for our purpose. Rather we ask: *Under what conditions will the shear components of* **T** *be real?* To investigate this question it is convenient to employ a new system of axes x', y', z' in the normal-stress space, where x' is orthogonal to the π-plane and y' and z' lie in the π-plane (Morgan,[1] § 7).

In terms of these new coordinates, Eqs. (12) have the form:

$$a_1(\sqrt{3}y' + z') + b_1 = (x' - c_1)^2,$$

$$a_2(-\sqrt{3}y' + z') + b_2 = (x' - c_2)^2, \tag{14}$$

$$-a_3 z' + b_3 = (x' - c_3)^2,$$

where the a's, b's, and c's are defined in Morgan,[1] § 7.

After eliminating z', by use of Eq. (14)₃, from Eqs. (11) we find that *all* of the shear stresses will be real if either one of the following *two* sets of inequalities is simultaneously satisfied:

$$\frac{1}{a_3}\left[x' - \left(c_3 - \frac{1}{\sqrt{2}}a_3\right)\right]^2 \geqslant K_{12} \left|\; \leqslant K_{12},\right.$$

$$\sqrt{3}y' + \frac{1}{a_3}[x' - (c_3 + \sqrt{2}a_3)]^2 \leqslant K_{13} \left|\; \geqslant K_{13},\right. \tag{15}$$

$$-\sqrt{3}y' + \frac{1}{a_3}[x' - (c_3 + \sqrt{2}a_3)]^2 \leqslant K_{23} \left|\; \geqslant K_{23},\right.$$

where

$$K_{12} = \frac{\sqrt{6}}{2}\frac{D_3}{A_3}, \qquad K_{13} = \frac{\sqrt{6}}{2}\left[\frac{D_3}{A_3} + f_{13} - f_{23}\right],$$

$$K_{23} = \frac{\sqrt{6}}{2}\left[\frac{D_3}{A_3} - f_{13} + f_{23}\right].$$

TABLE II

PROPERTIES OF THE INEQUALITY SETS $(15)_1$ AND $(15)_2$ [a]

CASE	D_3	A_3	$\dfrac{D_3}{A_3}$	SATISFACTION OF SETS $(15)_1$ & $(15)_2$	REMARKS
I_1		> 0	< 0	NOT POSSIBLE	No real solutions possible
I_2	< 0	$= 0$	$\pm \infty$	NOT POSSIBLE	No real solutions possible
I_3		< 0	> 0	NOT POSSIBLE	No real solutions possible
II_1		> 0	0	POSSIBLE	At three isolated points, at each of which $t_{12} = t_{13} = t_{23} = 0$
II_2	$= 0$	$= 0$	$0/0$	POSSIBLE	At one isolated point, at which $t_{12} = t_{13} = t_{23} = 0$
II_3		< 0	0	POSSIBLE	At three isolated points, at each of which $t_{12} = t_{13} = t_{23} = 0$
III_1		> 0	> 0	POSSIBLE	Fig. 1
III_2	> 0	$= 0$	$\pm \infty$	POSSIBLE	Special Case of Fig. 2
III_3		< 0	< 0	POSSIBLE	Similar to Fig. 1

[a] From Morgan.[1]

The controlling parameters are D_3 and A_3. Our results as to the possibility of satisfying these inequality sets are summarized in Table II. Only cases III are of interest. The situation for case III_1 is shown in Fig. 1. This figure shows that the two sets of inequalities can be simultaneously satisfied only for those values of the normal stresses which are within the two shaded curvilinear triangular regions on the parabolic surface. Thus, if the line defined by Eqs. $(13)_{1,2}$ does not intersect one or the other or both of these triangular regions, then no real shear-stress solutions are possible.

5. A Special Case

We now consider a very interesting special case. We suppose that the response functions $\hat{\delta}$ and $\hat{\varepsilon}$ vanish identically so that the coefficient tensor $\mathfrak{D}$ reduces to

$$\mathfrak{D} = \tfrac{1}{2}\gamma \mathbf{I}. \tag{16}$$

In this case, with $E_\Delta \equiv \psi_0 + \psi_1 B_\Delta + \psi_2 B_\Delta^2$, the diagonal solutions are

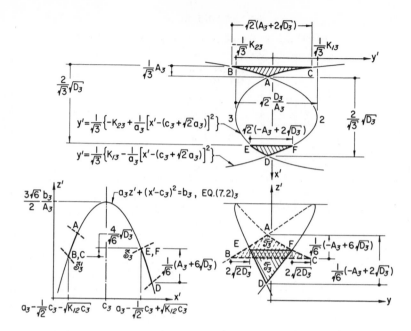

FIG. 1. Regions on the parabolic surface $(14)_3$ within which all shear stresses are real. Notes: 1. Positive directions indicated by arrows on dimension lines; 2. Figure drawn for $A_3 > 0$, not to scale. (From Morgan.[1])

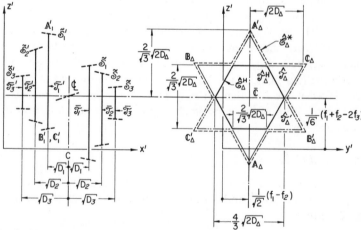

FIG. 2 Nomenclature: Various regions and surfaces for the isotropic media defined in Section 5 (large deformation case). Notes: 1. Typical cross section shown. 2. $A_1 = A_2 = A_3 = 0$. (From Morgan.[1])

given by

$$t_{\Delta\Delta} = \frac{1}{2\gamma}\{-[1 + 2(\alpha B_\Delta + \beta B_\Delta{}^2)] \pm \sqrt{[1 + 2(\alpha B_\Delta + \beta B_\Delta{}^2)]^2 + 4\gamma E_\Delta}\}$$

$$\equiv -f_\Delta \pm \sqrt{D_\Delta} \tag{17}$$

and if, for $\Delta = 1, 2, 3, |4\gamma E_\Delta| \ll |1 + 2(\alpha B_\Delta + \beta B_\Delta{}^2)|^2$ then branch 1 is the constitutive equation for isotropic finite elasticity.

Let

$$C = \frac{1}{2\gamma}\{3 + 2[\alpha I_B + \beta(I_B{}^2 - II_B)]\}. \tag{18}$$

We find that the parabolic surfaces (12) degenerate (since $A_\Delta = 0$, $\Delta = 1, 2, 3$) into the three pairs of parallel planes

$$I_T \equiv t_{11} + t_{22} + t_{33} = \begin{cases} -C \pm \sqrt{D_1}, \\ -C \pm \sqrt{D_2}, \\ -C \pm \sqrt{D_3}. \end{cases} \tag{19}$$

On each of these planes we find that there are closed triangular regions within which the shear stresses are all real. These are shown in Fig. 2. The degree of determinancy obtained in the general case is lost in this case. *Any* point within these regions can now be used to obtain real shear stresses. These, in turn, can only be produced by an appropriate specification of the surface tractions.

6.   Characteristic Surfaces for the Medium†

Employing the results for this special case we can show that characteristic surfaces for these media can be constructed in the principal-stress space.

As the deformation changes the boundaries of each of the triangular regions shown in Fig. 2 will sweep out tubelike surfaces ($\tilde{\mathfrak{S}}_\Delta$, $\tilde{\mathfrak{S}}_\Delta'$, $\Delta = 1, 2, 3$) in the principal-stress space. These surfaces will have equilateral triangular cross sections in an $x' = $ const plane. Consider the traces of these surfaces in any $x' = $ const plane which intersects them. Take the union and intersection of the regions ($\hat{\mathfrak{I}}_\Delta$, $\hat{\mathfrak{I}}_\Delta'$, $\Delta = 1, 2, 3$) in the $x' = $ const plane bounded by these traces. Outside of the surface ($\tilde{\mathfrak{S}}^*$)

---

† See Morgan,[1] § 12 for a detailed discussion.

formed by these unions ($\hat{\mathbb{C}}*$) no real shear stresses can be obtained irrespective of what the deformation may be. In the region between the surface $\hat{\mathfrak{S}}*$ and that ($\hat{\mathfrak{S}}^H$) formed by the intersections $\hat{\mathbb{C}}^H$ there will always be some value of the deformation which will produce imaginary shear stresses. But, within the region bounded by the surface $\hat{\mathfrak{S}}^H$ no imaginary shear stresses are obtained for any value of the deformation.

Under our assumption as to the behavior of the coefficient tensors, we now consider what happens to these surfaces in the limit of zero deformation. Then all six triangular regions will coalesce in pairs to the two triangular regions shown in Fig. 3. Note that their "center" is now on the x'-axis. For small deformations, the intersection of these two regions will be the hexagon $\overline{\mathbb{C}}^H$ shown in Fig. 3. This hexagon, except for a 30° rotation, has an appearance similar to that of the Tresca initial yield locus.†

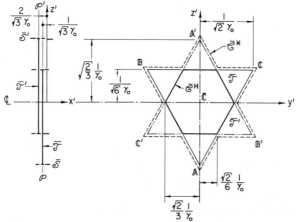

Fig. 3   Nomenclature: Various regions and surfaces for the isotropic media defined in Section 5 (small deformation case). Notes: 1. Not to scale. 2. $\gamma_0 \gg 1$. (From Morgan.[1])

The surface of intersections which we have defined then looks very much like one of the yield surfaces used in plasticity theory, since it satisfies the symmetry and convexity requirements in the limit of small deformations. Additionally, we note that this surface in the principal stress space can be such that it closes at two points along the x'-axis, one above and the other below the π-plane. An investigation of this possibility is given in Morgan,[1] § 9.

† In fact $\overline{\mathbb{C}}^H$ is exactly similar to the "outer hexagon" referred to in Naghdi[6] p. 132 as: "... not a well-known yield condition...."

7. Conclusions

In conclusion, we have exhibited a correctly set constitutive equation whose properties are such that it may be said to possess characteristic surfaces in the principal-stress space. For the special case considered here it is interesting to note that the cross section of one of these surfaces in a plane parallel to, and in the vicinity of, the π-plane has an appearance similar to that of one of the yield-loci used in plasticity theory. Other cross sections might be likened to "hardening rules."

Clearly, the general properties we have exhibited will carry over for constitutive equations of the same form stated in terms of two tensors: one kinetic and the other kinematic; for example, stress and stretching tensors.

From another point of view, the results obtained may be taken to be indicative of the additional wide variety of material response which is possible when the physically imperative requirements of constitutive invariance (or, material objectivity) and dimensional homogeneity are (as *must* be the case) satisfied by constitutive equations, while (at the onset) abandoning the conditions imposed by the "principle of determinism of stress,"† (Noll,[2] § 12; Truesdell and Noll,[3] § 26). This principle can, of course, be invoked at a later stage of the analysis. In the present instance, for example, to avoid ambiguities, branch 1 of Eq. (17) may be chosen as the appropriate constitutive equation for the situation being considered, Morgan[1] § 12. In general, the particular choice made will be determined by physical requirements related to the problem under investigation.

REFERENCES

1. A. J. A. Morgan, Some properties of media defined by constitutive equations in implicit form. *Intern. J. Eng. Sci.* **4**, 155–178 (1966).
2. W. Noll, A mathematical theory of the mechanical behavior of continuous media, *Arch. Rational Mech. Anal.* **2**, 197–226 (1958).
3. C. Truesdell and W. Noll, The nonlinear field theories of mechanics, *in* "Handbuch der Physik" (S. Flügge, ed.), Vol. III/3. Springer, Berlin, 1965.
4. A. J. A. Morgan, On the construction of constitutive equations for continuous media, *Arch. Mech. Stosowanej* **17**, 145–174 (1965).
5. R. S. Rivlin and J. L. Ericksen, Stress-deformation relations for isotropic materials, *J. Rational Mech. Anal.* **4**, 323–425 (1955).
6. P. M. Naghdi, "Plasticity." Pergamon Press, Oxford, 1960.

† Which may be regarded as implying that Eq. (2) is *uniquely* invertible for **T** in terms of **B** for *all* values of **B**.

Cosserat Continua

W. JAUNZEMIS

Department of Engineering Mechanics
Pennsylvania State University
University Park, Pennsylvania

1. Introduction

In field theories the method of "natural" (or, intrinsic) geometries appears very attractive to some, while others view it with indifference or even distrust. But although the choice of methods may be a matter of some controversy, the importance of the problem of formulating suitable geometric models of "material spaces" is unquestioned. Continuum mechanics is of course not the only discipline concerned with such models. For instance, the Cosserat theory of media which are made up of "oriented" particles is formally analogous to Einstein's theory of Riemann spaces admitting a distant parallelism.[1] In each case the assignment of intrinsic frames of reference to points of space provides a means of describing certain features automatically, i.e., by virtue of the geometric model on which the theory rests. In Einstein's theory the intrinsic frames were used to incorporate electromagnetism into the general theory of gravitation; in the Cosserat theory dislocations, for instance, are already a part of the geometric make-up of bodies.

It is easy to become enticed by the siren songs of differential geometry of general spaces, and be led to expect a great deal from the adaption of geometric results to the setting of continuum mechanics. However, Riemannian geometry alone does not suffice to formulate a plasticity theory, any more than Euclidean geometry would suffice to formulate an elasticity theory. Constitutive equations are needed, and it is here that often theories which start from a broad geometric basis either stop or make very specialized assumptions. This does not happen by choice, of course; the kind of phenomena that one wishes to describe, e.g., plastic flow caused by moving dislocations, have remained intractable for a good many years now. The advances in continuum mechanics during the past two decades have largely bypassed the mechanical behavior of metals. In fact, the groping of dislocationists towards a deeper theory of plasticity has been, when viewed from the awesome heights of modern continuum mechanics, an easy target of criticism. Still, the dislocations are there, waiting to be described by a continuum theory.

2. Cosserat Continua

We can visualize a Cosserat continuum as a medium whose particles are oriented by means of orthonormal triads of "directors" $\mathbf{d}_a$, $a = 1, 2, 3$. In the end it may be only the tensors constructed from director fields that matter, but that is unimportant right now.

To illustrate the new deformation measures, let us consider elementary beam theory from the point of view of one-dimensional Cosserat continua.[2] A "Cosserat beam" is a collection of thin slices, the cross sections, mounted on a perfectly flexible center line. Since the cross sections are assumed to be rigid, they can be replaced by directors $\mathbf{d}$. The "strains of orientation" are: the rotation γ of $\mathbf{d}$ relative to the unit normal vectors $\mathbf{v}$ of the center line, and the gradient of the angles P describing the absolute rotation of directors (Fig. 1). The shear resistance is related to γ, the bending resistance to the gradient of P.

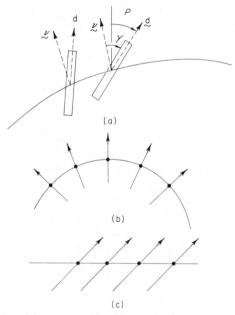

Fig. 1   (a) "Cosserat beam." (b) Bending without shearing. (c) Shearing without bending. (Letters with tildes beneath them in figure are equivalent to bold face letters in text.)

In a three-dimensional Cosserat continuum the point deformation is described in the usual way:

$$x_i = x_i(\mathbf{X}, t),$$

where x_i and X_i are the final and initial coordinates of a particle. Locally, a deformation is characterized by the deformation gradients

$$F_{im} = \partial x_i / \partial X_m .$$

We also note the "polar decomposition" of **F** into an orthogonal tensor **R** and a positive symmetric tensor **U**:

$$\mathbf{F} = \mathbf{RU}.$$

The rotation of director triads is described by a field of orthogonal tensors **P**. To **R** and **U** we can now adjoin the deformation tensors

$$\mathbf{A} = \mathbf{P}^{-1}\mathbf{F}, \qquad k_{ijk} = (\partial_j P_{km}) P_{mi}^{-1} .$$

The rotation gradients are constructed in the same way as one would construct an angular velocity $\boldsymbol{\Sigma}$ of director frames: $\boldsymbol{\Sigma} = \dot{\mathbf{P}}\mathbf{P}^{-1}$. The tensor **A** describes the local point deformation as seen from director triads; in particular, $\boldsymbol{\gamma} = \mathbf{P}^{-1}\mathbf{R}$ is the rotation of directors relative to the underlying "point continuum." In a linearized theory we let $\mathbf{F} = (1 + \tilde{\mathbf{R}})(1 + \tilde{\mathbf{E}}) \approx 1 + \tilde{\mathbf{E}} + \tilde{\mathbf{R}}, \mathbf{P} = 1 + \tilde{\mathbf{P}}$, where $\tilde{\mathbf{E}}$ is the infinitesimal strain tensor, and $\tilde{\mathbf{R}}$ and $\tilde{\mathbf{P}}$ are now skew-symmetric. Then

$$k_{ijk} = -\partial_j \tilde{P}_{ik}, \qquad \boldsymbol{\varepsilon} \equiv \mathbf{A} - 1 = \tilde{\mathbf{E}} + (\tilde{\mathbf{R}} - \tilde{\mathbf{P}}).$$

The deformations **A** and **k** give rise to a stress **T** and a couple stress **M**, both **T** and **M** being asymmetric. In the absence of body forces and body couples the equations of motion can be written as

$$\partial_j T_{ji} = \rho \dot{v}_i, \qquad \partial_j M_{ji} + \varepsilon_{ijk} T_{[jk]} = \rho \dot{\eta}_i,$$

where ε_{ijk} denotes the alternator, ρ is the mass density, and **v** and $\boldsymbol{\eta}$ are, respectively, velocity and intrinsic angular momentum. The latter may be of the form $\eta_i = I_{ij}\Sigma_j$, where I_{ij} is the inertia tensor of an "oriented particle." It is also instructive to look at the energy balance relating density of internal energy, u, heat flux **q**, and the stress power:

$$\rho \dot{u} - \text{div } \mathbf{q} = T_{(ij)} \partial_j v_i + \varepsilon_{ijk} T_{[ij]}(\omega_k - \Sigma_k) + M_{ji} \partial_j \Sigma_i,$$

$$\boldsymbol{\omega} = \tfrac{1}{2} \text{curl } \mathbf{v}.$$

If $\boldsymbol{\omega} = \boldsymbol{\Sigma}$, for instance, then $T_{[ij]}$ are, not unlike stresses in a rigid body, workless constraint forces. Similarly, $T_{(ij)}$ and M_{ji} are workless constraint forces if $\partial_{(j}v_{i)} = 0$ and $\partial_j \Sigma_i = 0$, respectively. These observations provide possible interpretations of the stresses. Thus, if we suppose that oriented particles represent rough grains, then couple stresses would describe frictional couples acting on the grains.

An elasticity theory of Cosserat continua has been studied by many authors, notably Mindlin,[3] Toupin,[4] and Hehl and Kroener.[5]

In the linearized theory the stress relations are of the form

$$\mathbf{T} = \mathbf{T}(\varepsilon, \mathbf{k}), \qquad \mathbf{M} = \mathbf{M}(\varepsilon, \mathbf{k}),$$

whence it is easy to see that there exists now a material property l with the dimension of length. Namely, if μ is a material coefficient with the dimension of stress, then among other things we must have that

$$\mathbf{T} \sim \mu\varepsilon, \qquad \mathbf{M} \sim \mu l^2 \mathbf{k}.$$

This means that the theory can describe a number of phenomena which the "nonpolar" theory can not, e.g., dispersion of waves, boundary layer effects at surfaces.

Nowadays, there are general principles for obtaining general constitutive equations, but little help can be had in the design of special theories. This is a pity because the new "multipolar" theories bring with them more material coefficients than one knows what to do with. There is a kind of an "anti-equipresence" principle, called by Hamel a *Befreiungsprinzip*, which states that stresses depend, in the first place, on the kinematical variables which they would inhibit in a rigid motion. Accordingly, from inspection of the stress power terms in the energy balance we would obtain the following special laws† :

$$T_{(ij)} \sim \tilde{E}_{ij}, \qquad T_{[ij]} \sim \tilde{R}_{ij} - \tilde{P}_{ij}, \qquad M_{ji} \sim \varepsilon_{imn}\,\partial_j \tilde{P}_{mn}$$

for solids, and

$$T_{(ij)} \sim \partial_{(j}v_{i)}, \qquad \varepsilon_{ijk}T_{[ij]} \sim \omega_k - \Sigma_k, \qquad M_{ji} \sim \partial_j \Sigma_i$$

for fluids.

To return to dislocations, let us note that the field of directors defines an intrinsic parallelism. Since this parallelism is a property of the Cosserat continuum, we should determine the tensors which can be extracted from it. Now, a vector field $\mathbf{v}$ is constant with respect to the director triads if the components v_a are constants. In order to express the condition $\partial_j v_a = 0$ in Cartesian coordinates, we introduce the intrinsic derivatives $v_{i;j}$ by

$$v_{i;j} = d_{ai}\,\partial_j v_a = d_{ai}\,\partial_j d_{ak}v_k = \partial_j v_i + l_{kij}v_k,$$

where

$$l_{kij} = d_{ai}\,\partial_j d_{ak},$$

and d_{ai} are components of directors in the Cartesian coordinate system: $\mathbf{d}_a = d_{ai}\mathbf{e}_i$.

---

† A dependence of T_{ij} upon k_{ijk} may be excluded by material symmetry, as in centrosymmetric crystals.

Evidently, l_{kij} transform as tensor components in a change from one Cartesian coordinate system to another; the skew-symmetric part

$$t_{kij} = l_{k[ij]}$$

may be referred to as a torsion tensor (or, "tensor of dislocation density").

In order to interpret the role of t_{kij}, let us consider the integrability of the "anholonomic" differentials $d_1(x)_a = d_{ai} d_1 x_i$. Starting from $d_2 d_1(x)_a = (\partial_j d_{ai}) d_2 x_j d_1 x_i$, we are led to a "Burgers vector"

$$b_k \equiv d_{ak}[d\,d(x)_a] = d_{ak}[d_2 d_1(x)_a - d_1 d_2(x)_a] = -t_{kij} da_{ij},$$

where

$$da_{ij} = d_1 x_i d_2 x_j - d_2 x_i d_1 x_j$$

is an area element spanned by the vectors $d_1\mathbf{x}$ and $d_2\mathbf{x}$. Similarly, if $\mathbf{D}_a$ denote directors in their initial configuration, then, starting from $d(X)_a = D_{ai} dX_i$, we arrive at

$$B_k = D_{ak}[d\,d(X)_a] = -T_{kij} dA_{ij}.$$

Assuming that only changes of the Burgers vector matter, we let $\mathbf{D}_a$ be a constant field, so that $t_{kij} = -k_{[ij]k}$. If we replace t_{kij} by

$$\alpha_{mk} = \varepsilon_{ijm} t_{kij},$$

and k_{ijk} by

$$k_{pj} = \tfrac{1}{2}\varepsilon_{ikp} k_{ijk},$$

then it follows that

$$\alpha_{mk} = k_{mk} - \delta_{mk} k_{jj},$$

i.e., the tensor of dislocation density is in essence the same as the tensor of rotation gradients. If instead of an orthogonal tensor $\mathbf{P}$ we use a general second rank tensor $\boldsymbol{\phi}$, as is done in the case of a *dipolar medium*, then

$$k_{ijk} = (\partial_j \phi_{km})\phi_{mi}^{-1}$$

has no skew-symmetries, so that, aside from dislocation density, k_{ijk} now also describe certain gradients of "micro-strains."

According to the second viewpoint the knowledge of both dislocation densities t_{kij} and T_{kij} is necessary, hence the appropriate strain measure is in effect the difference of t_{kij} and T_{kij}. Consequently, both dislocation densities must be referred to the same "observer." Thus, in addition to

$d(x)_a = d_{ai} dx_i$ we should introduce $D(x)_a \equiv D_{ai} dx_i$, i.e., for the sake of comparison both configurations of directors should be superimposed on the same neighborhood dx_i. Then, letting

$$D_2 D_1(x)_a = (\partial_j D_{ai}) d_2 x_j d_1 x_i, \quad \bar{B}_k = D_{ak}[D\, D(x)_a] = -f_{k[ij]} da_{ij},$$

we arrive at

$$b_k - B_k = (f_{k[ij]} - t_{kij})\, da_{ij}.$$

Here $f_{k[ij]} - t_{kij}$ is a "strain of dislocation."

The Burgers vectors, or, equivalently, the dislocation density α must be connected up with the displacement field. In the linearized theory the procedure is as follows. The total displacement gradients are decomposed into "elastic" and "plastic" parts:

$$\partial_j u_i = \varepsilon_{ij}^E + \varepsilon_{ij}^P.$$

One then assumes

$$\operatorname{curl} \varepsilon^E = \alpha = -\operatorname{curl} \varepsilon^P,$$

so that, for given α, the determination of stresses reduces to problems of residual stresses. Writing

$$\dot{\alpha}_{ji} = -\varepsilon_{jks} \partial_k \dot{\varepsilon}_{si}^P,$$

Mura[1] relates the plastic strain rate to a tensor of dislocation movement, V_{ijk},† by setting up a balance equation for α:

$$\frac{d}{dt} \int_S \alpha_{ji} n_j\, da = \oint_{\partial S} \varepsilon_{jkm} V_{jki}\, dx_m.$$

Then from $\dot{\alpha}_{mi} = \varepsilon_{mrs} \varepsilon_{jks} \partial_r V_{jki}$ it follows that $\partial_r \dot{\varepsilon}_{si}^P = -\varepsilon_{sjk} \partial_r V_{jki}$. It seems that in this field one is inclined to make whatever assumptions are necessary to be able to derive the equations of conventional plasticity theory. Thus, Mura assumes in effect that $V_{[jk]i} \sim \varepsilon_{jkm} T_{mi}$, which enables him to obtain the usual flow rule right away.

3. Dipolar Media

In generalizing the Cosserat model described in what preceded, there seems to be little merit in considering deformable director triads (unless, of course, the directors admit a concrete interpretation, e.g., as position

† The tensor V_{ijk} may be of the form $V_{ijk} = V_i \alpha_{jk}$, where V denotes the velocity field of the moving dislocations. Cf. Kroener.[7]

vectors in a cell of a nonprimitive lattice). Rather, it is natural to replace the orthogonal tensor $\mathbf{P}$ by a general second rank tensor $\boldsymbol{\phi}$, thus arriving at a dipolar medium. A family of deformation measures can then be constructed as follows:

Point deformation $\qquad \mathbf{F} \to \mathbf{F}^T \mathbf{F}$

"Relative" deformation $\quad \mathbf{A} = \boldsymbol{\phi}^{-1}\mathbf{F}$

Micro-deformation $\qquad \boldsymbol{\phi} \to \boldsymbol{\phi}^T\boldsymbol{\phi}, \qquad k_{ijk} = (\partial_j\phi_{km})\phi_{mi}^{-1}$.

A general method for generating equations of motion of multipolar media has been given by Green and Rivlin,[8] so that the main open problem is again the derivation of appropriate constitutive equations. Here one should be able to draw upon lattice dynamics and phenomenological dislocation theory.

REFERENCES

1. A. Einstein, Auf die Riemann-Metrik und den Fern-Parallelismus gegründete einheitliche Feldtheorie, *Math. Ann.* (*Berlin*) **102** (1929).
2. W. Günther, Zur Statik und Kinematik des Cosseratschen Kontinuums, *Abh. Braunschw. Wiss. Ges.*, 195–213 (1958).
3. R. D. Mindlin, Micro-structure in linear elasticity, *Arch. Rational Mech. Anal.* **16**, 51–78 (1964).
4. R. A. Toupin, Theories of elasticity with couple-stress, *Arch. Rational Mech. Anal.* **17**, 85–112 (1964).
5. F. Hehl and E. Kröner, Zum Materialgesetz eines elastischen Mediums mit Momentenspannungen, *Z. Naturforsch.* **20a**, 336–350 (1965).
6. T. Mura, Continuous distribution of dislocations and the mathematical theory of plasticity, *Phys. Stat. Sol.* **10**, 447 (1965).
7. E. Kröner, "Kontinuumstheorie der Versetzungen und Eigenspannungen," p. 26. Springer Verlag, Berlin, 1958.
8. A. E. Green and R. S. Rivlin, Multipolar continuum mechanics, *Arch. Rational Mech. Anal.* **17**, 113–147 (1964).

Stability of Couette Flow of Second-Order Fluids between Two Coaxial Circular Cylinders†

SUBHENDU K. DATTA‡

Department of Aerospace Engineering Sciences
University of Colorado
Boulder, Colorado

In this paper the stability or instability of an incompressible second-order fluid in Couette flow between two coaxial circular cylinders has been considered. The gap between the cylinders has been taken to be arbitrary. The Galerkin approximate technique has been used to get the approximate values of the critical Taylor number. A full comparison has been made with the corresponding case of an ordinary viscous fluid and the changes in stability characteristics that are caused by the elasticity of the liquid have been pointed out. This suggests new experiments for determining the elastico-viscous parameters.

1. Introduction

The constitutive equations for an incompressible second-order fluid are given by

$$T_{ij} + p\delta_{ij} = \alpha_1 A_{(1)ij} + \alpha_2 A_{(1)ik}A_{(1)kj} + \alpha_3 A_{(2)ij}, \tag{1.1}$$

where T_{ij} is the stress tensor, δ_{ij} is the Kronecker delta, p is a scalar, α_1, α_2, α_3 are material constants. The tensors $A_{(n)ij}$ are Rivlin–Ericksen tensors given by

$$A_{(1)ij} = v_{i,j} + v_{j,i},$$
$$A_{(n)ij} = A_{(n-1)ik}v_{k,j} + A_{(n-1)jk}v_{k,i} + \dot{A}_{(n-1)ij}, \tag{1.2}$$

the superimposed dot denoting the material time derivative. Equation (1.1) can be obtained§ from Noll's[1] definition of incompressible simple fluids with the use of certain assumptions of smoothness that follow

† This work was supported by the Advanced Research Projects Agency, Aerodynamics Contract DA31-124-ARO-D-139.

‡ Present address: Department of Aeronautical Engineering, Indian Institute of ~~Higher~~ Technology, Kanpur, India.

§ See, for example, B. D. Coleman and W. Noll, *Ann. N.Y. Acad. Sci.* **89**, 672 (1961).

73

from the physical concept of "gradually fading memory." Equation (1.1) includes the corrections for viscoelastic effects correct to order two in the time scale. Markovitz and Coleman[2–4] have considered several steady and unsteady flows of second-order incompressible fluids. From their analysis there emerge several possible experimental methods of determining the constants α_2, α_3. Markovitz and Brown[5] performed some experiments with polyisobutylene solutions in cetane. They made normal stress measurements and obtained values of α_2, α_3.

However, not much attention has been paid to the analysis of stability of steady laminar flows that have been considered by Markovitz and Coleman.[2,3] Stability of parallel flows and cylindrical Couette flows have been studied extensively in literature[6,7] and one becomes curious to know how the elasticity of a fluid may change the stability characteristics. Also, such analysis may suggest possible experiments to characterize a simple fluid. Since it is known that even for Newtonian fluids the stability analysis is mathematically quite involved, so it is expected that for a general viscoelastic fluid such an analysis will be extremely involved and complicated. However, to gain an insight and some experience about the changes in the stability characteristics that are caused by the elasticity of the fluid, it seems worthwhile to consider a second-order fluid whose constitutive equations are given by (1.1). Naturally, the validity of such an analysis will be confined in those fluids which have short memories. But this helps us to gain to some extent a better understanding of the flows of a simple fluid and this also suggests some new experiments to measure the parameters α_2, α_3. Previously, we[8,9] have considered the stability of elastico-viscous fluids in cylindrical Couette flows and have found that the elasticity of the fluid influences to a great extent the stability or instability of such flows. For the sake of simplicity, we confined our attention to the case when the gap between the cylinders is small. But it was found that the gap-width could play an important role in modifying the stability or instability of the flow. So in the present paper we have considered the case where the gap is arbitrary. We find that the dependence of the critical Taylor number (for the onset of instability) on the gap-width and the ratio of angular velocities of the cylinders is quite different from that in the case of Newtonian fluids. Since the characteristic differential equations are quite complicated in this general case, it is not apparent that one can get an exact solution. So we have used the Galerkin approximate technique (using polynomial approximants) to get the eigenvalues of the problem. This technique has been successfully used by Tsao,[10] and DiPrima et al.[11] for finding the critical Taylor number for the onset of instability in cylindrical Couette flows with or without temperature gradients across the cylinders. The success of the technique in these analyses and comparison with our previous small-gap analysis lead us to believe that for small values of the elastico-viscous parameters our results give the true behavior within the limits of numerical accuracy. Experiments in these directions would be quite helpful in establishing the accuracy of our results and they will also be able to determine the values of α_2 and α_3.

2. Equations

We shall consider Eq. (1.1) together with the equations of motion, which, in the absence of body forces, are

$$T^i_{j,j} = \rho\left(\frac{\partial v^i}{\partial t} + v^i_{,j}, v^j\right), \tag{2.1}$$

and the equation of continuity

$$v^i_{,i} = 0. \tag{2.2}$$

Suppose the fluid is confined between two long coaxial circular cylinders of radii R_1, R_2, which are rotating with angular velocities Ω_1, Ω_2, respectively. Consider cylindrical polar coordinates (r, θ, Z) with Z-axis along the axis of the cylinders. In this case, Eqs. (2.1) together with (1.1), (1.2), and (2.2) admit steady state solutions of the forms:

$$v^1 = v^3 = 0, \qquad v^2 = V = Ar + Br^{-1}, \tag{2.3}$$

where

$$A = -\Omega_1\frac{\eta^2 - \mu}{1 - \eta^2}, \qquad B = \Omega_1\frac{(1 - \mu)R_1^{\,2}}{1 - \eta^2}, \qquad \mu = \frac{\Omega_2}{\Omega_1}, \qquad \eta = \frac{R_1}{R_2}.$$

Our problem will be to consider the conditions for stability of the basic flow (2.3) to small axisymmetric disturbances. Let the velocity components of a particle in the disturbed state be

$$v^1 = u(r, Z, t), \qquad v^2 = V + v(r, Z, t),$$
$$v^3 = w(r, Z, t), \qquad p = P + p^1(r, Z, t), \tag{2.4}$$

where P is the pressure in the steady state. Assume u, v, w, p^1 to be so small that their products and higher powers may be neglected. Then Eqs. (2.1) can be linearized by keeping only first powers of u, etc.

To analyze this linearized system of equations obtained from (2.1) we will use the normal mode analysis, i.e., it will be assumed first that

$$u(r, Z, t) = u(r, Z)e^{\sigma t}, \qquad v(r, Z, t) = v(r, Z)e^{\sigma t},$$
$$w(r, Z, t) = w(r, Z)e^{\sigma t}, \qquad p^1(r, Z, t) = p^1(r, Z)e^{\sigma t}. \tag{2.5}$$

The motion is stable if the real part σ_1 of σ is negative and unstable if it is positive. We will consider the marginal state when $\sigma_1 = 0$ and the imaginary part σ_2 of σ is not necessarily zero. Using (2.5) we can obtain the physical components of the stress tensor T_{ij}.† Finally, let us assume:

$$u(r, Z) = u(r) \sin \lambda Z, \qquad v(r, Z) = v(r) \sin \lambda Z,$$
$$w(r, Z) = w(r) \cos \lambda Z, \qquad p^1 = p^*(r) \sin \lambda Z. \tag{2.6}$$

Here $2\pi/\lambda$ is a wavelength of the disturbance. With these assumptions the disturbance equations can be simplified to give

$$(DD_* - a^2)Lu = Ta^2\left[\Phi(x) + \frac{1-\mu}{\xi^2}\left\{K(D^2 - a^2) - \frac{2K_1}{\xi}D + \frac{K_2}{\xi^2}\right\}\right]v, \tag{2.7}$$
$$Lv = \left[1 - \frac{(1-\mu)K_3}{(\eta^2 - \mu)\xi^2}(DD_* - a^2)\right]u,$$

together with the boundary conditions

$$u = Du = v = 0 \qquad \text{at} \quad x = \pm\tfrac{1}{2}. \tag{2.8}$$

Here

$$\xi = \frac{r}{R_2} = \eta_0 + \varepsilon x, \qquad \eta_0 = \tfrac{1}{2}(1 + \eta), \quad \varepsilon = 1 - \eta,$$

$$D \equiv d/dx, \qquad D_* \equiv d/dx + \varepsilon/\xi, \qquad K_1 = (\alpha_2 + \alpha_3)/\rho d^2,$$

$$L \equiv (DD_* - a^2)(1 + iN\beta) - i\beta, \qquad N = \alpha_3/\rho d^2, \quad d = R_2 - R_1,$$

$$\beta = \sigma_2 d^2/v, \qquad v = \alpha_1/\rho, \qquad K_2 = \varepsilon(3K_1 + N), \qquad K_3 = \eta^2 K_1,$$

$$K = (K_1 + N)/2\varepsilon, \qquad a = \lambda d,$$

$$T = \frac{8A^2 d^4(i - \eta)}{v^2(1 - \mu/\eta^2)}, \qquad \Phi(x) = \frac{1}{2\varepsilon}\left[1 - \mu/\eta^2 - \frac{1-\mu}{\xi^2}\right].$$

Equations (2.7) together with Eqs. (2.8) define an eigenvalue problem with T (Taylor number) considered as eigenvalue parameter. Our problem is to find a real β for a given a, μ, K_1, N such that T is real. Then

† See Datta.[9]

varying a we get the minimum value of T for given μ, K_1, and N. This minimum T gives the critical Taylor number T_c for the onset of instability; the corresponding critical values a_c and β_c define the critical wave number and frequency parameter, respectively. It should be noted that if we take the limit $\eta \to 1$ of Eqs. (2.7) and assume that K, K_1, N are finite then we shall get our[8] Eqs. (2.9)–(2.10).

3. Solution

Equations (2.7) will be solved approximately by Galerkin's method. Let $\{u_i\}$ and $\{v_i\}$ be a complete set of functions with $u_i \varepsilon c^4(-\frac{1}{2}, \frac{1}{2})$ and $v_i \varepsilon c^2(-\frac{1}{2}, \frac{1}{2})$ and satisfying the boundary conditions

$$u_i(\pm\tfrac{1}{2}) = Du_i(\pm\tfrac{1}{2}) = 0, \qquad v_i(\pm\tfrac{1}{2}) = 0.$$

Write

$$u = \sum_1^\infty a_i u_i, \qquad v = \sum_1^\infty b_i v_i \tag{2.9}$$

and assume that these series are termwise differentiable. Then u, v will satisfy the boundary conditions (2.8). Substituting (2.8) in (2.7) we shall get

$$(DD_* - a^2)L\left(\sum_1^\infty a_i u_i\right) - Ta^2\left[\Phi(x) + \frac{1-\mu}{\xi^2}\left\{K(D^2 - a^2)\right.\right.$$

$$\left.\left. - \frac{2K_1}{\xi}D + \frac{K_2}{\xi^2}\right\}\right]\left(\sum_1^\infty b_i v_i\right) = Eu(x), \tag{2.10}$$

$$L\left(\sum_1^\infty b_i v_i\right) - \left[1 - \frac{(1-\mu)K_3}{(\eta^2-\mu)\xi^2}(DD_* - a^2)\right]\left(\sum_1^\infty a_i u_i\right) = Ev(x).$$

It is now required that the errors $Eu(x)$ and $Ev(x)$ be orthogonal to the functions ξu_i and ξv_i, i.e.,

$$\int_{-1/2}^{1/2} \xi Eu(x)u_i\, dx = 0,$$

$$i = 1, 2, \ldots, \infty \tag{2.11}$$

$$\int_{-1/2}^{1/2} \xi Ev(x)v_i\, dx = 0.$$

In practice we keep only a finite number, say n, of terms in (2.9). Then from (2.10), using (2.11), we shall get $2n$ linear homogeneous equations

and the condition for existence of the nontrivial solution of this system
is that the determinant

$$
\begin{vmatrix}
F_{ij} & \vdots & TG_{ij} \\
\cdots & \vdots & \cdots \\
H_{ij} & \vdots & I_{ij}
\end{vmatrix} = 0, \qquad i,j = 1, 2, \ldots, n. \tag{2.12}
$$

Here

$$
F_{ij} = \int_{-1/2}^{1/2} \xi[(DD_* - a^2)Lu_j]u_i \, dx,
$$

$$
G_{ij} = -\int_{-1/2}^{1/2} \xi u_i a^2 \left[\Phi(x) + \frac{1-\mu}{\xi^2} \left\{ K(D^2 - a^2) + \frac{2K_1}{\xi}D + \frac{K_2}{\xi^2} \right\} \right] v_j \, dx,
$$

$$
H_{ij} = \int_{-1/2}^{1/2} \xi v_i \left[1 - \frac{(1-\mu)K_3}{(\eta^2 - \mu)\xi^2}(DD_* - a^2) \right] u_j \, dx,
$$

$$
I_{ij} = -\int_{-1/2}^{1/2} \xi v_i L u_j \, dx.
$$

Equation (2.12) will be an nth degree equation for T and the lowest
positive root of this equation for given μ, η, K_1, N and over-all values
of a will give us the nth approximation to the critical Taylor number T_c.
It may reasonably be expected that if one takes more and more terms
in (2.9) then this approximate value will tend to the true value T_c in the
limit. In our present analysis we have taken $n = 2$ to save the computing
time. However, it is expected that for small K_1 and N this second approximation will be a reasonably good one. In Tables I–V we give the
values of $T_c^{(2)}$, $a_c^{(2)}$, and $\beta_c^{(2)}$ for different η, μ, K_1, and N.

4. Conclusion

To check the accuracy of the results obtained in this paper we note
the following: for $K_1 = 0.01$, $N = -0.01$, we get, when $\eta = 0.95$,†

μ	a_c	T_c	a_c (Small gap)	T_c (Small cap)
0.5	3.35	1769.40	3.30	1905.5
0.0	3.30	2750.00	3.30	2791.5
-0.5	3.45	5620.00	3.40	5370.3

† From Datta.[9]

The corresponding values for $K_1 = 0.0$, $N = 0.0$ are[†]

μ	a_c	T_c	a_c (Small gap)	T_c (Small gap)
0.5	3.12	2183.3	3.12	2275.3
0.0	3.13	3328.6	3.12	3390.3
−0.25	3.15	4480.1	3.13	4462.6

The comparison between these two tables leads us to believe that our present results are reasonably good. We believe that the reason for the larger difference between T_c at $\eta = 0.95$ and T_c for small gap analysis for $K_1 \neq 0$, $N \neq 0$, is possibly the fact that all the terms depending on these parameters are multiplied by $(1 - \mu)$. Besides, if we look at the second equation of (2.7) we notice that there can be a slightly larger discrepancy from the factor $(1 - \mu)/(\eta^2 - \mu)$ that multiplies K_3.

TABLE I
$K_1 = 0.01$, $N = -0.01$

η	μ	K_2	K_3	K	a_c	T_c	β_c
0.95	0.8	0.001	0.010	0.00	3.45	1315.89	0.0
0.95	0.5	0.001	0.010	0.00	3.35	1769.40	0.0
0.95	0.2	0.001	0.010	0.00	3.34	2268.30	0.0
0.95	0.0	0.001	0.010	0.00	3.30	2750.0	0.0
0.95	−0.25	0.001	0.010	0.00	3.32	3750.0	0.0
0.95	−0.50	0.001	0.010	0.00	3.45	5620.0	0.0
0.85	0.8	0.003	0.007	0.00	9.20	−9162.0	0.0
0.85	0.5	0.003	0.007	0.00	3.44	1355.0	0.0
0.85	0.2	0.003	0.007	0.00	3.35	1950.0	0.0
0.85	0.0	0.003	0.007	0.00	3.40	2455.0	0.0
0.85	−0.50	0.003	0.007	0.00	3.50	6026.0	0.0
0.75	0.5	0.005	0.006	0.00	4.00	692.88	0.0
0.75	0.2	0.005	0.006	0.00	3.40	1584.00	0.0
0.75	0.0	0.005	0.006	0.00	3.38	2140.00	0.0
0.75	−0.25	0.005	0.006	0.00	3.40	3450.00	0.0
0.75	−0.50	0.005	0.006	0.00	3.60	7250.00	0.0
0.55	0.5	0.009	0.002	0.00	12.0	−14044.0	0.0
0.55	0.2	0.009	0.002	0.00	3.6	811.0	0.0
0.55	0.0	0.009	0.002	0.00	3.4	1656.0	0.0
0.55	−0.25	0.009	0.002	0.00	3.4	4266.0	0.0
0.55	−0.50	0.009	0.002	0.00	5.0	88973.9	0.0

[†]From Tsao.[10]

Subhendu K. Datta

TABLE II

$$K_1 = 0.02, \quad N = -0.01$$

η	μ	K_2	K_3	K	a_c	T_c	β_c
0.95	0.8	0.002	0.018	0.10	4.65	649.0	0.0
0.95	0.5	0.002	0.018	0.10	5.25	530.00	0.0
0.95	0.2	0.002	0.018	0.10	6.00	399.95	0.0
0.95	0.0	0.002	0.018	0.10	6.00	340.82	0.0
0.95	-0.25	0.002	0.018	0.10	6.25	287.00	0.0
0.95	-0.50	0.002	0.018	0.10	6.50	245.00	0.0
0.95	-1.00	0.002	0.018	0.10	7.50	182.80	0.0
0.85	0.90	0.007	0.014	0.033	19.0	-20893.0	0.0
0.85	0.80	0.007	0.014	0.033	9.2	-1888.0	0.0
0.85	0.70	0.007	0.014	0.033	5.5	192.8	0.0
0.85	0.60	0.007	0.014	0.033	4.7	572.8	0.0
0.85	0.50	0.007	0.014	0.033	4.6	671.9	0.0
0.85	0.40	0.007	0.014	0.033	4.6	721.1	0.0
0.85	0.30	0.007	0.014	0.033	4.9	737.9	0.0
0.85	0.20	0.007	0.014	0.033	5.0	739.5	0.0
0.85	0.0	0.007	0.014	0.033	5.3	716.2	0.0
0.85	-0.25	0.007	0.014	0.033	6.0	675.2	0.0
0.85	-0.50	0.007	0.014	0.033	6.5	623.7	0.0
0.85	-0.75	0.007	0.014	0.033	7.0	574.2	0.0
0.75	0.5	0.012	0.011	0.02	5.0	315.42	0.0
0.75	0.2	0.012	0.011	0.02	4.5	750.00	0.0
0.75	0.0	0.012	0.011	0.02	4.85	810.00	0.0
0.75	-0.25	0.012	0.011	0.02	5.75	885.00	0.0
0.75	-0.5	0.012	0.011	0.02	6.75	890.00	0.0
0.75	-0.75	0.012	0.011	0.02	7.8	871.00	0.0
0.75	-1.00	0.012	0.011	0.02	9.0	825.7	0.0
0.55	0.5	0.022	0.006	0.011	11.5	-2558.5	0.0
0.55	0.4	0.022	0.006	0.011	8.0	- 810.3	0.0
0.55	0.3	0.022	0.006	0.011	5.5	13.49	0.0
0.55	0.2	0.022	0.006	0.011	4.7	389.1	0.0
0.55	0.0	0.022	0.006	0.011	4.8	812.8	0.0
0.55	-0.25	0.022	0.006	0.011	6.0	1220.7	0.0
0.55	-0.5	0.022	0.006	0.011	11.0	1440.4	0.0
0.55	-0.75	0.022	0.006	0.011	20.0	1429.0	0.0
0.55	-1.00	0.022	0.006	0.011	-	1349.0	0.0

TABLE III

$K_1 = 0.03, \quad N = -0.01$

η	μ	K_2	K_3	K	a_c	T_c	β_c
0.95	0.8	0.004	0.027	0.20	6.25	347.5	0.0
0.95	0.5	0.004	0.027	0.20	7.50	237.5	0.0
0.95	0.2	0.004	0.027	0.20	8.00	166.2	0.0
0.95	0.0	0.004	0.027	0.20	8.00	138.7	0.0
0.95	-0.25	0.004	0.027	0.20	8.25	113.0	0.0
0.95	-0.50	0.004	0.027	0.20	8.50	96.2	0.0
0.85	0.9	0.012	0.022	0.066	20.0	-7980.0	0.0
0.85	0.8	0.012	0.022	0.066	10.0	- 823.3	0.0
0.85	0.7	0.012	0.022	0.066	7.0	99.93	0.0
0.85	0.6	0.012	0.022	0.066	6.3	305.5	0.0
0.85	0.5	0.012	0.022	0.066	6.0	359.8	0.0
0.85	0.3	0.012	0.022	0.066	6.8	366.4	0.0
0.85	0.2	0.012	0.022	0.066	7.0	354.5	0.0
0.85	0.0	0.012	0.022	0.066	7.7	319.9	0.0
0.85	-0.25	0.012	0.022	0.066	8.0	281.9	0.0
0.85	-1.00	0.012	0.022	0.066	9.2	201.7	0.0
0.75	0.5	0.02	0.017	0.04	7.0	166.88	0.0
0.75	0.2	0.02	0.017	0.04	6.0	396.05	0.0
0.75	0.0	0.02	0.017	0.04	7.5	404.00	0.0
0.75	-0.25	0.02	0.017	0.04	8.5	388.00	0.0
0.75	-0.50	0.02	0.017	0.04	9.0	358.00	0.0
0.55	0.5	0.036	0.009	0.022	14.0	-1056.00	0.0
0.55	0.3	0.036	0.009	0.022	8.0	6.74	0.0
0.55	0.2	0.036	0.009	0.022	7.0	212.1	0.0
0.55	0.0	0.036	0.009	0.022	8.0	415.9	0.0
0.55	-0.25	0.036	0.009	0.022	-	489.8	0.0
0.55	-0.50	0.036	0.009	0.022	-	495.4	0.0
0.55	-1.00	0.036	0.009	0.022	-	446.7	0.0

TABLE IV

$K_1 = 0.01$, $N = -0.02$

η	μ	K_2	K_3	K	a_c	T_c	β_c
0.95	0.8	0.0005.	0.009	-0.1	2.80	2234.0	0.0
0.95	0.5	0.0005	0.009	-0.1	1.40	14290.0	0.0
0.85	0.5	0.001	0.007	-0.033	2.75	2239.0	0.0
0.85	0.2	0.001	0.007	-0.033	2.15	6309.0	0.0
0.85	0.0	0.001	0.007	-0.033	1.50	22694.7	0.0
0.75	0.5	0.002	0.006	-0.02	3.2	955.00	0.0
0.75	0.2	0.002	0.006	-0.02	2.65	2985.00	0.0
0.75	0.0	0.002	0.006	-0.02	2.10	6607.00	0.0
0.75	-0.25	0.002	0.006	-0.02	1.00	79101.40	0.0
0.55	0.2	0.004	0.003	-0.011	3.10	1122.00	0.0
0.55	0.0	0.004	0.003	-0.011	2.65	2951.00	0.0
0.55	-0.25	0.004	0.003	-0.011	1.45	45710.00	0.0

TABLE V[a]

$\alpha_2 = 0.118$, $\alpha_3 = -0.0445$,[b] $R_2 = 10$ cm

η	μ	K_1	K_2	K_3	N	K	a_c	T_c	β_c
0.95	0.8	0.381	0.046	0.344	-0.23	1.50	–	4.50	0.0
0.95	0.5	0.381	0.046	0.344	-0.23	1.50	–	2.80	0.0
0.95	0.0	0.381	0.046	0.344	-0.23	1.50	–	1.60	0.0
0.95	-0.25	0.381	0.046	0.344	-0.23	1.50	–	1.30	0.0
0.95	-0.50	0.381	0.046	0.344	-0.23	1.50	–	1.10	0.0
0.75	0.70	0.015	0.009	0.009	-0.009	0.012	4.60	436.5	0.0
0.75	0.50	0.015	0.009	0.009	-0.009	0.012	4.30	1216.0	0.0
0.75	0.00	0.015	0.009	0.009	-0.009	0.012	4.70	1419.0	0.0
0.75	-0.5	0.015	0.009	0.009	-0.009	0.012	5.5	1585.0	0.0
0.75	-1.0	0.015	0.009	0.009	-0.009	0.012	8.5	1636.6	0.0

[a] 3.90% polyisobutylene solution in cetane.
[b] These values have been taken from Markovitz and Brown.[5]

Next let us analyze the variation of T_c with μ for given η, K_1, and N. We find that if η is close to 1, then T_c decreases as μ decreases when K is positive and for $K \leqslant 0$ the behavior is opposite. However, if $K > 0$ as η departs more and more from 1, T_c first increases as μ decreases, if $\mu < \eta^2$. However, if $\mu > \eta^2$, then $- T_c$ decreases as μ decreases. In the range of μ values that we have considered ($\mu \geqslant -1$) we find that if $1 - \eta$ is not too large then T_c starts decreasing again as μ approaches -1. The value of μ for which T_c attains a maximum moves beyond -1

as η decreases. If K increases then this maximum point moves to the right of $\mu = -1$. We also note that if K is positive and η is small, the flow can be unstable for values of μ greater than η^2 but close to this value. We have found that such a motion is unstable to disturbances of small wavelengths, although the critical Taylor number is quite high. This is quite a distinct behavior of the elastico-viscous liquids. For, we know that for an ordinary viscous liquid the flow is stable if $\mu > \eta^2$. It can be observed from Tables II, III, and IV that if either K is large and positive or if η is small and μ is negative (with $K_1 > 0$, $K > 0$) then the critical wave number is quite large; in fact it goes to infinity as μ decreases, i.e., T approaches T_c asymptotically. This is consistent with our[8] previous observations. We also observe that if K is negative then the flow is stable to disturbances of small wavelengths and that if η is close to 1 then the flow is quite stable except for values of μ close to η^2. However, the flow becomes more and more unstable as η decreases. From Table V it is clear that the Couette flow of polyisobutylene solution in cetane is quite unstable (note that if $\eta = 0.95$, $R_2 = 10$ cm, then $d = 0.5$ cm). In Figs. 1–5 we have shown the variations of T_c and a_c with η and μ for different values of K_1 and N.

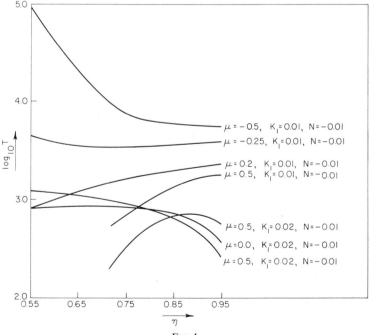

FIG. 1

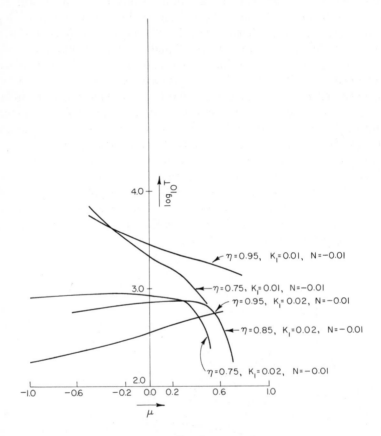

FIG. 2

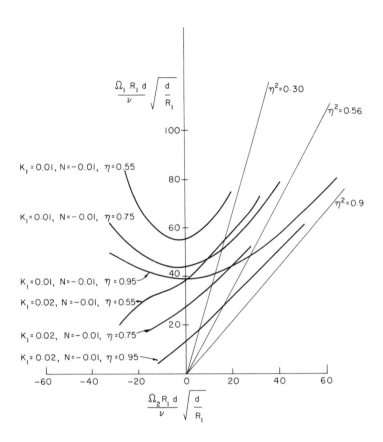

FIG. 3

Subhendu K. Datta

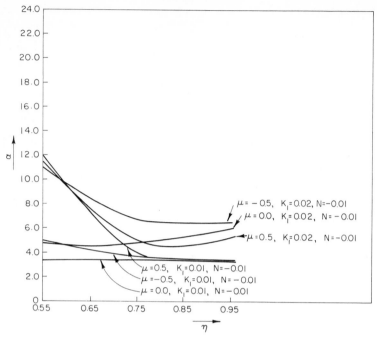

Fig. 4

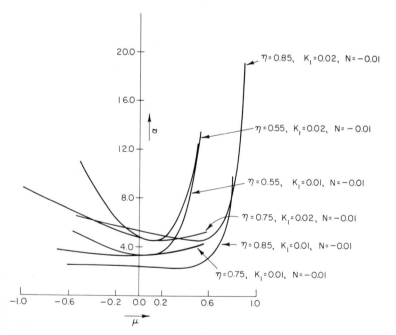

Fig. 5

REFERENCES

1. W. Noll, *Arch. Rational Mech. Anal.* **2**, 197 (1958).
2. B. D. Coleman and H. Markovitz, *J. Appl. Phys.* **35**, 1 (1964).
3. H. Markovitz and B. D. Coleman, *Advan. Appl. Mech.* **8**, 69 (1964).
4. H. Markovitz and B. D. Coleman, *Phys. Fluids* **7**, 833 (1964).
5. H. Markovitz and D. Brown, *Trans. Soc. Rheology* **7**, 137 (1963).
6. S. Chandrasekhar, "Hydrodynamic and Hydromagnetic Stability." Oxford Univ. Press, London and New York, 1961.
7. C. C. Lin, "The Theory of Hydrodynamic Stability." Cambridge Univ. Press, London and New York, 1955.
8. S. K. Datta, *Phys. Fluids* **7**, 1915 (1964).
9. S. K. Datta, *Proc. 2nd Tech. Meeting Soc. Eng. Sci.* (to be published).
10. S. Tsao, Stability of Flow between Arbitrarily Spaced Concentric Cylindrical Surfaces and Related Mathematical Problems, Ph.D. Thesis, Rensselaer Polytechnic Institute, Troy, New York, 1963.
11. J. Walowit, S. Tsao, and R. C. DiPrima, *J. Appl. Mech.* (1964).

Approximate Constitutive Equations†

A. C. PIPKIN
Division of Applied Mathematics
Brown University
Providence, Rhode Island

1. Introduction

Constitutive equations are not exact descriptions of even the gross physical properties of real materials. The best that can be said of any mathematical model of material behavior is that it provides a useful description of certain features of the behavior of some real materials, under limited conditions of operation. Although this is well known, the proviso with respect to operating conditions is easy to forget. Because of the wide range of operating conditions implicit in the term *viscoelastic flow*, the study of viscoelastic flows is particularly susceptible to the confusion which can arise when one ignores the role of operating conditions. Stress-deformation relations of various types proliferate and, appearing to be mutually contradictory, compete unnecessarily for acceptance.

Viscoelastic flow includes, as some limiting cases, linear and nonlinear elastic deformation, linear viscoelastic behavior, and Newtonian and non-Newtonian viscous flow. One given material may, under various circumstances, exhibit all of these types of behavior and other types as well. If the behavior of a given material is to be described with quantitative accuracy under all such circumstances by one inclusive constitutive equation, then that equation is likely to be somewhat complex.

Constitutive equations of exceeding complexity and generality are available in the literature. These equations are not usually suitable for use, in their full generality, in the solution of initial and boundary value problems. The purpose of such equations is to provide a framework within which observed behavior under a wide range of conditions can be correlated, and to serve as sources of simpler equations valid under more narrowly prescribed conditions of flow. Within such a framework, various types of seemingly contradictory special equations can be

† The work described in this paper was carried out under a grant DA-ARO(D)-31-124-G484 from the Army Research Office, Durham, North Carolina.

reconciled, as narrow-range approximate descriptions. The urge for generality is appeased by the complex wide-range description, and the urge for simplicity by the narrow-range approximations.

Some caution must be exercised in the use of narrow-range approximations. It is customary and comfortable to regard a constitutive equation as defining an idealized material, whose behavior under all conditions of operation is described by that same constitutive equation. This convention is useful and for many purposes inescapable, but it should not be adopted when dealing with second- or higher-order approximations. A second-order approximation is likely to lead to absurd results if applied to flow conditions outside the range for which the equation was intended, even if the corresponding first approximation produces no absurdity. In Section 14 we comment further on this apparent paradox.

The purpose of the present review is to give some examples showing how various simpler constitutive equations of disparate forms arise as narrow-range approximations to a complicated wide-range description. In order to avoid notational and operational complexities which are not relevant to the main object of the paper, we restrict our attention to one-dimensional unsteady shearing motions, and consider only the shearing stress. Almost all of the examples which we discuss are available in three-dimensional form in the cited references, or in the review by Rivlin.[1]

In Section 2 we first discuss the notion of wide-range and narrow-range approximations, in terms of the Navier–Stokes equations. We then turn to the consideration of viscoelastic flows, and in particular to the memory functional constitutive equations of Green and Rivlin[2] and Noll[3] (Section 4). In order to give a more explicit form to this framework, we suppose that the memory functional involved in the stress-deformation relation can be expanded in a convergent series of multiple integrals, similar to the representation introduced by Green and Rivlin[2] (Section 6).

A number of restricted types of flows and the constitutive equations appropriate to each type are discussed in Sections 7 to 13. In particular, we consider small motions (Section 7), short motions (Section 8), and slow motions (Section 9), with some emphasis on the role of the stress-relaxation time in classifying flows according to duration, rate, and smoothness. These examples illustrate the fact that the terms *first-order*, *second-order*, etc., have meaning only when one has defined just what is small in the family of flows considered. To emphasize this point, we consider in Section 10 various orderings of approximations in problems of slow smooth motion.

Although the examples considered in Sections 7 to 10 include linear viscoelasticity (small motions), nonlinear elasticity (short motions), and Newtonian flow (slow motions), they can all be regarded as equations valid for perturbations on a state of rest. In Sections 11 to 13 we consider perturbations on given motions. In particular, we discuss small motions superposed on stress-relaxation at constant strain (Section 12), and small perturbations on steady simple shearing motions (Section 13).

In closing, we discuss a few examples illustrating the absurdities which can arise from the misuse of approximate equations, emphasizing the fact that second-order approximations lead to inconsistencies more easily than first-order approximations do.

2. Wide-Range and Narrow-Range Descriptions

The choice of a mathematical model to describe the behavior of a given material under specified circumstances is not entirely a mathematical problem, but predominantly a matter for experience and judgement to decide. However, the element of judgement can be decreased by using, at least at the outset, a description whose range of validity is very wide.

Classical fluid dynamics affords a simple example of the use of a relatively wide-range equation. The Navier–Stokes constitutive equation may be written in the form

$$\sigma_{ij} = -p(\rho, T)\,\delta_{ij} + \lambda(\rho, T)\varepsilon_{kk}\,\delta_{ij} + 2\mu(\rho, T)\varepsilon_{ij}, \qquad (2.1)$$

although the viscosities λ and μ are not generally considered to be functions of the density ρ. This relation applies to such a wide range of flow conditions in air and water that it is easy to forget that there are any restrictions at all on its range of validity.

However, fluid dynamical problems are rarely solved on the basis of the complete equation (2.1). The equations most widely used are

$$\sigma_{ij} = -p\,\delta_{ij}, \qquad (2.2)$$

$$\sigma_{ij} = -p(\rho, T)\,\delta_{ij}, \qquad (2.3)$$

and

$$\sigma_{ij} = -p\,\delta_{ij} + 2\mu\varepsilon_{ij}, \qquad (2.4)$$

the constitutive equations for perfect incompressible flow, perfect compressible flow, and viscous incompressible flow. Each of these three equations has a range of validity in problems involving air and in problems involving water.

The main purpose of the wide-range description (2.1) is to provide a framework within which the simpler equations (2.2)–(2.4) can be regarded as compatible, as narrow-range approximations with more or less specific ranges of validity. If (2.1) were not available, one might reasonably conclude that some real materials are described by (2.2), others by (2.3), and still others by (2.4). With (2.1) available, it is seen that the relations (2.2)–(2.4) can describe various aspects of the behavior of one and the same material, the choice depending as much on operating conditions as on the nature of the material.

Remarks of this kind apply with even more force when nonlinear viscoelastic behavior is to be considered.

3. One-Dimensional Shearing Motions

In the discussion of viscoelastic flows which follows, for simplicity we consider only one-dimensional shearing motions. In such a motion, each fluid particle moves parallel to the x-axis with a velocity which is independent of x and z. The particle located at $x(0)$, y, z at time zero is located at $x(y, t)$, y, z at time t, where $x(y, t) = x(0) + f(y, t)$. The shear κ is defined in terms of the displacement $f(y, t)$ by

$$\kappa(y, t) = f_y(y, t). \tag{3.1}$$

We usually write $\kappa(t)$ for the shear, letting the dependence on y be tacitly understood.

The displacement of a particle at time τ relative to its position at time t is

$$x(y, \tau) - x(y, t = f(y, \tau) - f(y, t), \tag{3.2}$$

and the shear at time τ relative to the configuration at time t is

$$\kappa(\tau, t) = \partial[f(y, \tau) - f(y, t)]/\partial y = \kappa(\tau) - \kappa(t). \tag{3.3}$$

The shear rate is given in various equivalent forms by

$$\kappa_\tau(\tau, t) = \kappa'(\tau) = u_y(y, \tau), \tag{3.4}$$

where u is the velocity.

4. Materials with Memory

We suppose that the stress at any given particle at time t is determined by the displacement gradients at that particle at times up to and including t. We omit the dependence of stress on temperature for simplicity. Only the shearing stress $\sigma = \sigma_{xy}$ will be considered. Our assumption is that

$$\sigma(t) = \mathfrak{F}'' \left[\kappa \left(t \underset{\tau=0}{\overset{\infty}{-}} \tau \right) \right], \tag{4.1}$$

where $\mathfrak{F}''$ is a functional of the shear history $\kappa(t - \tau)(\tau \geqslant 0)$. The relation (4.1) is the special form taken by the constitutive equation of Green and Rivlin[2] and Noll[3] for the presently considered case.

The constitutive assumptions embodied in (4.1) apply to solids as well as to fluids. Noll[3] showed that since a fluid has no preferred configuration, the strain measure should be a strain relative to the configuration at the instant of measurement of stress. Thus, for a fluid, the relation (4.1) should take the more special form

$$\sigma(t) = \mathfrak{F}' \left[\kappa \left(t \underset{\tau=0}{\overset{\infty}{-}} \tau, t \right) \right], \tag{4.2}$$

where $\kappa(\tau, t)$ is the relative shear defined in (3.3). We note that since $\kappa(t, t)$ is zero by definition, the history $\kappa(t - \tau, t)$ $(\tau \geqslant 0)$ can be determined when $\kappa'(\tau) = \kappa_t(\tau, t)(\tau \leqslant t)$ is known. Consequently, $\sigma(t)$ can be expressed equally well as a functional of the shear rate

$$\sigma(t) = \mathfrak{F} \left[\kappa' \left(t \underset{\tau=0}{\overset{\infty}{-}} \tau \right) \right]. \tag{4.3}$$

Indeed, in the present special case we might have taken this as our primitive assumption.

Noll[3] also pointed out that if the stress depends on nothing other than the relative displacement gradients, then the material must be isotropic. In the present case, isotropy means that the functional $\mathfrak{F}$ is odd:

$$\mathfrak{F} \left[-\kappa' \left(t \underset{\tau=0}{\overset{\infty}{-}} \tau \right) \right] = -\mathfrak{F} \left[\kappa' \left(t \underset{\tau=0}{\overset{\infty}{-}} \tau \right) \right]. \tag{4.4}$$

In particular, the shearing stress in a fluid which has always been at rest must vanish:

$$\mathfrak{F} \left[\underset{\tau=0}{\overset{\infty}{0}} \right] = 0. \tag{4.5}$$

Restrictions imposed by isotropy on the stress functional in the full three-dimensional case have been derived by Green and Rivlin,[2] and Green et al.[4] (See also Rivlin,[1] and Wineman and Pipkin.[5])

5. Materials with Fading Memory

As a general restriction on the nature of the functional $\mathfrak{F}$ in (4.3), we suppose that in a fluid, the stress at a given instant is negligibly affected by the distant past history of the deformation. Thus, for example, suppose that the fluid is brought from rest into a state of steady shearing motion at the rate $\kappa'(\tau) = \gamma$. We assume that as time progresses, the influence of the initial rest state fades, and the stress approaches a value which can depend only on γ. Isotropy implies that this limiting stress is an odd function of γ, say $\sigma = \gamma\eta(\gamma^2)$.

As a second example of the fading memory assumption, suppose that the fluid is at rest until time zero, when it is quickly sheared by the amount κ_0 and then held at rest again. We first suppose that at times large in comparison to the time required for the shearing, the stress becomes independent of the details of the transition from $\kappa(0) = 0$ to κ_0, and can thus depend on κ_0 and t only, say $\sigma(t) = R(\kappa_0, t)$. The function $R(\kappa_0, t)$, extrapolated to $t = 0$, is the response to an ideal stepfunction shear history. We now assume further that the longer the shear is held fixed at the value κ_0, the more nearly the stress approaches that in a fluid which has always been at rest, i.e.

$$R(\kappa_0, t) \to 0 \qquad \text{as} \quad t \to \infty.$$

These examples show that in certain restricted classes of motions, the fading memory assumption alone is sufficient to allow a complete characterization of the relevant material properties, for example the stress-relaxation function $R(\kappa_0, t)$ and the apparent viscosity $\eta(\gamma^2)$. Constitutive equations for other classes of motions with restricted time-dependence have been discussed by Rivlin.[6] Some nontrivial problems can be solved on the basis of such limited information, for example the viscometric flow problems treated by Rivlin,[7] Criminale et al.,[8] Ericksen,[9] and Coleman and Noll,[10] or the problems of stress-relaxation at constant strain considered by Rivlin.[11]

6. Viscoelastic Fluids

To proceed further, it would be desirable to make more specific physical postulates about the behavior of the material considered, and to deduce the exact mathematical restrictions imposed on the functional $\mathfrak{F}$ by these postulates. However, the best efforts in this direction have not succeeded in placing any strong restrictions on the form of the functional. Hence, in order to give a more tangible structure to the theoretical framework, we will make some mathematical rather than physical assumptions about the form of the functional.

It will be seen that a model of the following kind is capable of describing a wide range of types of behavior. We suppose that the functional can be expanded as a convergent series of multiple integrals, analogous to the Taylor series expansion of an analytic function:

$$\sigma(t) = \sum_{n \text{ odd}} \int_0^\infty \cdots \int_0^\infty K_n(\tau_1, \cdots, \tau_n) \kappa'(t - \tau_1) \cdots \kappa'(t - \tau_n) \, d\tau_1 \cdots d\tau_n. \tag{6.1}$$

The restriction to odd-order integrals is a consequence of the isotropy condition (4.4). In keeping with the fading memory assumption, we suppose that K_n approaches zero when any one of its arguments approaches infinity. More restrictively, we assume that K_n is of negative exponential order with respect to each of its arguments. We also suppose that the kernels K_n are functions, not distributions, and we will be willing to make any smoothness assumptions about them which may be found to be useful.

It is not to be expected that the series (6.1) will be convergent for every strain history of interest. However, we suppose that the representation (6.1) can be extended by analytic continuation to histories not within the original radius of convergence (see Sections 11–13).

It is not possible to derive a representation of the form (6.1) from any number of *a priori* physical postulates. Green and Rivlin[2] have shown that if a small change in the strain history produces only a small change in the stress, then the stress functional can be approximated by a terminating sum of integrals of the type (6.1). This result is analogous to the approximation of a continuous function by a polynomial, rather than the representation of an analytic function by its Taylor series expansion. Coleman and Noll[12] obtained the first term of the expansion by assuming existence of the first Frechet differential. In terms of functions, this is analogous to the assumption that a function is once differentiable, while our present assumption corresponds to infinite differentiability.

With restriction to histories which are not too badly behaved in the distant past, the integrals in (6.1) can be expressed in terms of the relative shear $\kappa(\tau, t)$ rather than the shear rate $\kappa'(\tau)$, by integrating by parts and recalling that $\kappa(t, t) = 0$:

$$\kappa(t) = \sum_{n \text{ odd}} \int_0^\infty \cdots \int_0^\infty K_n{}'(\tau_1, \cdots, \tau_n) \kappa(t - \tau_1, t) \cdots \kappa(t - \tau_n, t) \, d\tau_1 \cdots d\tau_n, \tag{6.2}$$

where

$$K_n'(\tau_1,\ldots,\tau_n) = \frac{\partial^n K_n(\tau_1,\ldots,\tau_n)}{\partial \tau_1 \cdots \partial \tau_n}. \tag{6.3}$$

We note that there is no loss of generality in taking the kernel K_n to be symmetric with respect to interchange of its arguments. We will often use this property without explicitly mentioning it again.

In passing, we note that the apparent viscosity $\eta(\gamma^2)$ and the stress-relaxation function $R(\kappa_0, t)$, mentioned in Section 5, are given in terms of the kernels K_n by

$$\gamma\eta(\gamma^2) = \sum_{n\,\text{odd}} \gamma^n \int_0^\infty \cdots \int_0^\infty K_n(\tau_1,\ldots,\tau_n)\, d\tau_1 \cdots d\tau_n \tag{6.4}$$

and

$$R(\kappa_0, t) = \sum_{n\,\text{odd}} \kappa_0^n K_n(t,\ldots,t). \tag{6.5}$$

7. Small Motions

In cases in which the relative strain $\kappa(\tau, t)$ is small at all times, as in small amplitude vibrations, it may be sufficient to retain only one or two terms of the integral expansion, i.e.

$$\sigma(t) = \int_0^\infty K_1'(\tau)\kappa(t - \tau, t)\, d\tau$$

$$+ \int_0^\infty \int_0^\infty \int_0^\infty K_3'(\tau_1, \tau_2, \tau_3)\kappa(t - \tau_1, t)\kappa(t - \tau_2, t)$$

$$\times \kappa(t - \tau_3, t)\, d\tau_1\, d\tau_2\, d\tau_3 + \cdots. \tag{7.1}$$

We note that because the relative shear is dimensionless, the expansion (7.1) may in appropriate problems be treated as an expansion in powers of a dimensionless typical shear (see Section 10).

The first approximation, involving only the single integral, is similar in appearance to the stress-relaxation integral constitutive equation used in the theory of infinitesimal viscoelastic deformations (see, for example, Lee[13]). This is one of the main motivations for assuming the multiple integral expansion for the nonlinear case. The idea of using the relative strain $\kappa(\tau, t)$ to extend the linear viscoelastic relation to cases of viscoelastic flow is due to Coleman and Noll.[12]

Let T be a typical stress-relaxation time, i.e. a time such that each of the kernels K_n' is small in comparison to its initial value $K_n'(0,\ldots,0)$

whenever any one of its arguments is as large as T. We assume that T can be estimated directly from the stress-relaxation function $R(\kappa_0, t)$ mentioned in Section 5. Coleman and Noll[12] have pointed out (in more precise terms) that the approximation in terms of one or two integrals will be applicable if $\kappa(t - \tau, t)$ is small for $\tau < T$, even if the relative shear becomes very large for larger values of τ, as in slow steady shearing motion. In Section 9 we consider slow motions in more detail.

8. Short Motions

We now consider motions in which the total time of motion is short in comparison to the typical stress-relaxation time T. Because T can be of the order of microseconds or centuries, depending on the particular material considered, it should be emphasized that observations which are short in the present sense may be extremely short or extremely long by some external standard.

At times so short that no noticeable stress relaxation has yet taken place, the response of the material is that of an elastic solid (see, e.g., Lee and Kanter,[14] Coleman[15]). Let us suppose that the fluid is at rest until time zero, when some motion begins. The constitutive equation can then be written as

$$\sigma(t) = \sum_{n \text{ odd}} \int_0^t \cdots \int_0^t K_n(t - \tau_1, \ldots, t - \tau_n)\kappa'(\tau_1) \cdots \kappa'(\tau_n)\, d\tau_1 \cdots d\tau_n, \quad (8.1)$$

and it is evident that the behavior of the kernels K_n for values of their arguments greater than t is irrelevant. If t/T is small, then not enough time has elapsed for the moduli K_n to have changed markedly from their initial values. If we approximate each kernel by its initial value, and recall that $\kappa(0) = 0$, we obtain the elastic stress-strain relation

$$\sigma(t) = F_0[\kappa(t)], \quad (8.2)$$

where

$$F_0(\kappa) = \sum_{n \text{ odd}} \kappa^n K_n(0, \ldots, 0). \quad (8.3)$$

The three-dimensional form of the stress-strain relation for finite elastic deformations is discussed in the book by Green and Adkins,[16] for example.

We note trivially that if κ is sufficiently small, $F_0(\kappa)$ can be linearized with respect to κ to obtain the stress-strain relation of classical elasticity theory. We also note that if κ is not small, the series (8.3) may fail to be convergent. This is a failing of the expansion, and not a failing of the elastic approximation (8.2).

Higher orders of approximation are obtained by replacing the kernels K_n by their Taylor series expansions up to terms of specified degree. For example, by including terms of first degree, we obtain

$$\sigma(t) = F_0[\kappa(t)] + F_1[\kappa(t)] \int_0^t (t - \tau)\kappa'(\tau)\, d\tau, \qquad (8.4)$$

where

$$F_1(\kappa) = \sum_{n \text{ odd}} \kappa^{n-1}(d/dt)K_n(t, \ldots, t)|_{t=0}. \qquad (8.5)$$

By comparing (8.3) and (8.5) to the expression (6.5) for $R(\kappa_0, t)$, we find that

$$F_0(\kappa) = R(\kappa, 0) \qquad \text{and} \qquad F_1(\kappa) = R_t(\kappa, 0)/\kappa. \qquad (8.6)$$

The close relation between $R(\kappa, t)$ and the short-motion approximations breaks down in higher orders of approximation.

A closely related treatment of short motions has been given by Huang and Lee.[17] The idea of initially elastic response has been exploited in problems of wave propagation by Varley,[18] Coleman et al.,[19] and Coleman and Gurtin.[20] The latter authors worked directly in terms of the stress functional $\mathfrak{F}$ rather than the integral expansion.

9. Slow Motions

The fact that the lower-order integral approximations (7.1) apply to sufficiently slow motions is more apparent when the integrals are expressed in terms of the shear rate rather than the relative shear:

$$\sigma(t) = \int_0^\infty K_1(\tau)\kappa'(t - \tau)\, d\tau$$

$$+ \int_0^\infty \int_0^\infty \int_0^\infty K_3(\tau_1, \tau_2, \tau_3)\kappa'(t - \tau_1)\kappa'(t - \tau_2)$$

$$\times \kappa'(t - \tau_3)\, d\tau_1\, d\tau_2\, d\tau_3 + \cdots. \qquad (9.1)$$

If κ' is nearly constant over intervals of the order of a typical stress-relaxation time T, as well as being small in comparison to $1/T$, we obtain as the lowest-order approximation to (9.1) the Newtonian viscous relation

$$\sigma(t) = \kappa'(t)\int_0^\infty K_1(\tau)\, d\tau = \mu\kappa'(\tau) \qquad \text{(say)}. \qquad (9.2)$$

In motions which are smooth as well as slow, higher-order approximations are provided by the Rivlin–Ericksen[21] representation. We expand the shear rate in Taylor series as

$$\kappa'(t - \tau) = \sum_{n=0}^{\infty} \frac{1}{n!} (-\tau)^n \kappa^{(n+1)}(t), \tag{9.3}$$

and we suppose that the series converges and is equal to $\kappa'(t - \tau)$ for $\tau < T$ at least. By using (9.3) in (9.1), we obtain

$$\sigma(t)/\mu = \sum a_n \kappa^{(n)}(t) + \sum\sum\sum a_{mnp} \kappa^{(m)}(t)\kappa^{(n)}(t)\kappa^{(p)}(t) + \cdots, \tag{9.4}$$

where $a_1 = 1$, and

$$\mu a_n = \frac{(-1)^{n-1}}{(n-1)!} \int_0^{\infty} K_1(\tau)\tau^{n-1}\, d\tau, \tag{9.5}$$

$$\mu a_{mnp} = \frac{(-1)^{m+n+p-1}}{(m-1)!(n-1)!(p-1)!} \int_0^{\infty}\int_0^{\infty}\int_0^{\infty} K_3(\tau_1, \tau_2, \tau_3)\tau_1^{m-1}\tau_2^{n-1}\tau_3^{p-1}$$

$$\times\, d\tau_1\, d\tau_2\, d\tau_3, \tag{9.6}$$

and so on.

It should be pointed out that if the series representation of $\kappa'(t - \tau)$ has only a finite radius of convergence τ^*, say, then the series in (9.4) will in general be asymptotic with respect to T/τ^* rather than convergent.[22] This fact does not diminish the usefulness of the representation (9.4) to any significant extent if T/τ^* is small.

A more important observation is that the Taylor series (9.3) may fail to be equal to $\kappa'(t - \tau)$ even on its interval of convergence. The representation of $\sigma(t)$ in terms of time derivatives of κ evaluated at time t is of course not applicable unless the strain history over the interval $(t - T, t)$ can be reconstructed from knowledge of these derivatives. For example, in initial value problems in which the fluid starts from rest, the representation (9.4) will not be accurate during an initial interval of the order of T, because the Taylor series (9.3) gives no representation of the rest state, which is still remembered by the fluid during this initial interval. In such problems the integral representation (9.1) should be used.

In spite of these restrictions, the Rivlin–Ericksen representation (9.4) has a wide range of applicability, particularly to the problems of steady flow and steady-state oscillation which comprise the larger part of those problems which are solvable in Newtonian flow.

10.   Orders of Approximation in Slow Motion

In the expansion (9.4) we have not indicated which terms are to be regarded as first-order, second-order, and so on, because the choice is not unique. The relative sizes of the terms in (9.4) depends on the particular family of problems considered, and on precisely what is to be regarded as small in the flow. To make this more explicit, let us consider a special example.

In this section only, we use u', t', y', etc., for dimensional variables. We consider a semi-infinite body of fluid occupying the region $y' > 0$, and suppose that the boundary $y' = 0$ oscillates sinusoidally in the x' direction with displacement amplitude A and frequency ω. In terms of the velocity $u'(y', t')$, the boundary conditions are

$$u'(0, t') = A\omega \cos \omega t', \qquad u'(\infty, t') = 0.$$

We seek a steady-state periodic solution satisfying the momentum equation

$$\rho \, \partial u'/\partial t' = \partial \sigma'/\partial y'. \tag{10.1}$$

We seek approximate solutions valid when the flow is close to Newtonian in some sense. With the Newtonian approximation $\sigma' = \mu \, \partial u'/\partial y'$, it is found that the solution can be written in terms of a dimensionless function $u(y, t)$ in the form

$$u' = A\omega u(y, t), \qquad y = y'/L, \qquad t = \omega t', \tag{10.2}$$

where

$$L^2 = \mu/\rho\omega. \tag{10.3}$$

The stress is given in terms of a dimensionless stress σ by

$$\sigma' = (\mu A\omega/L)\sigma(y, t). \tag{10.4}$$

We will use the same dimensionless variables in the non-Newtonian problem. We also use the notation

$$u_y^{(n)} = \partial^n u/\partial y \, \partial t^{n-1}, \tag{10.5}$$

and note that

$$\kappa^{(n)}(t') = (A/L)\omega^n u_y^{(n)}, \ldots \qquad (10.6)$$

The coefficients a_n, a_{mnp}, etc., in (9.4) have dimensions of time to various powers. Let us define a characteristic time T by $T = |a_2|$, and introduce dimensionless coefficients b_n through the relations

$$a_n = b_n T^{n-1}, \qquad a_{mnp} = b_{mnp} T^{m+n+p-1}, \ldots \qquad (10.7)$$

By using (10.4), (10.6), and (10.7) in (9.4), we obtain

$$\sigma = \sum b_n \varepsilon^{n-1} u_y^{(n)} + (A/L)^2 \sum \sum \sum b_{mnp} \varepsilon^{m+n+p-1} u_y^{(m)} u_y^{(n)} u_y^{(p)}$$
$$+ O(\varepsilon^4 A^4/L^4), \qquad (10.8)$$

where

$$\varepsilon = \omega T. \qquad (10.9)$$

Various schemes of approximation now suggest themselves. We first consider the case in which $A \to 0$ with ω fixed. In terms of the dimensionless parameters A/L and ε, this is the case in which $A/L \to 0$ with ε fixed. With A/L as a small parameter, all of the terms in the first sum in (10.8) are lowest-order, and the entire triple sum appears in the next order of approximation. This indicates that the integral formulation (9.1) would be more appropriate, and also indicates that our order estimates based on the Newtonian solution may be in error for this case. Indeed, with a small typical shear A/L, the motion is more appropriately described as small than as slow.

Let us now consider cases in which $\omega \to 0$ with some other quantity fixed, such as A, A/L, $A\omega$, or $A\omega/L$. In terms of the parameters ε and A/L, we suppose that $\varepsilon \to 0$ with Q_N fixed, where Q_N is defined by

$$(A/L)^2 = Q_N \varepsilon^N. \qquad (10.10)$$

With (10.10), the relation (10.8) becomes

$$\sigma = \sum b_n \varepsilon^{n-1} u_y^{(m)} + Q_N \sum \sum \sum b_{mnp} \varepsilon^{N+m+n+p-1} u_y^{(m)} u_y^{(n)} u_y^{(p)} + \cdots . \qquad (10.11)$$

First suppose that $\omega \to 0$ with the displacement amplitude A fixed.[23] From (10.3) and (10.9) we obtain

$$(A/L)^2 = (\rho A^2/\mu T)\varepsilon, \qquad (10.12)$$

which is the case $N = 1$ of (10.10). In this case, the first few terms of (10.11) in increasing powers of ε are (recalling that $b_1 = a_1 = 1$)

$$\sigma = u_y^{(1)} + \varepsilon b_2 u_y^{(2)} + \varepsilon^2 b_3 u_y^{(3)} + \varepsilon^3 [b_4 u_y^{(4)} + Q_1 b_{111}(u_y^{(1)})^3] + O(\varepsilon^4). \quad (10.13)$$

Next consider a family of problems in which $\omega \to 0$ with the typical shear A/L fixed. This is the case $N = 0$ of (10.10), and the first few terms of (10.11) in increasing powers of ε are

$$\sigma = u_y^{(1)} + \varepsilon b_2 u_y^{(2)} + \varepsilon^2 [b_3 u_y^{(3)} + Q_0 b_{111} (u_y^{(1)})^3] + O(\varepsilon^3). \quad (10.14)$$

This particular ordering is also encountered in problems of slow steady motion (see, e.g., Coleman and Noll,[24] Langlois and Rivlin,[25] Caswell and Schwartz,[26] Giezekus[27]). Behavior predicted by the three-dimensional form of the second-order approximation ($O(\varepsilon)$) has been treated in detail by Markovitz and Coleman.[28] This approximation has been widely misapplied to flows which are not slow in any sense.

Now suppose that $\omega \to 0$ with the velocity amplitude $A\omega$ fixed. In this case, $\varepsilon \to 0$ with Q_{-1} fixed. The relation (10.11) yields

$$\sigma = u_y^{(1)} + \varepsilon [b_2 u_y^{(2)} + Q_{-1} b_{111} (u_y^{(1)})^3] + O(\varepsilon^2). \quad (10.15)$$

As a final example, suppose that $\omega \to 0$ with the typical shear rate $A\omega/L$ fixed. From (10.10) we find that this is the case in which $\varepsilon \to 0$ with Q_{-2} fixed. In this case, the coefficient of ε^0 in (10.11) consists of all terms which involve only $u_y^{(1)}$. Thus, at an arbitrary shear rate but small unsteadiness ε, the constitutive equation $\sigma = \gamma \eta(\gamma^2)$ for steady shearing motion is appropriate as the lowest order of approximation, with $\gamma = u_y^{(1)}$. Higher approximations take the form

$$\sigma = \gamma \eta(\gamma^2) + \varepsilon \gamma' \eta_2(\gamma^2) + \varepsilon^2 [\gamma'' \eta_3(\gamma^2) + (\gamma')^2 \gamma \eta_4(\gamma^2)] + O(\varepsilon^3), \quad (10.16)$$

where $\gamma' = u_y^{(2)}$, etc. We note that because Newtonian flow is not the lowest-order approximation in this case, our order estimates based on the Newtonian solution may be in error. However, the formal analysis has indicated a more appropriate lowest-order approximation. The three-dimensional form of the constitutive equation for steady shearing motions (viscometric flows) is given by Criminale et al.[8] The corresponding forms of the higher approximations indicated by (10.16) are not available in the literature.

11. Analytic Continuation

Situations sometimes arise in which the stress corresponding to some simplestrain history $\kappa_0(t - \tau, t)$ ($\tau \geqslant 0$) is known, and it is desired to relate the stress for some close-by history $\kappa(t - \tau, t)$ ($\tau \geqslant 0$) to that for the base history $\kappa_0(t - \tau, t)$ ($\tau \geqslant 0$). We express $\kappa(t - \tau, t)$ in the form

$$\kappa(t - \tau, t) = \kappa_0(t - \tau, t) + \Delta\kappa(t - \tau, t). \quad (11.1)$$

The integral expansion (6.1) then yields

$$\sigma(t) = \sum_{p=0}^{\infty} \int_0^{\infty} \cdots \int_0^{\infty} \bar{K}_p\left[\kappa_0'\left(t - \underset{\xi=0}{\overset{\infty}{\xi}}\right); \tau_1, \ldots, \tau_p\right] \Delta\kappa'(t - \tau_1) \cdots$$

$$\times \Delta\kappa'(t - \tau_p)\, d\tau_1 \cdots d\tau_p, \tag{11.2}$$

where

$$\bar{K}_p\left[\kappa_0'\left(t - \underset{\xi=0}{\overset{\infty}{\xi}}\right); \tau_1, \ldots, \tau_p\right]$$

$$= \sum_{n\,\text{odd}} \binom{n}{p} \int_0^{\infty} \cdots \int_0^{\infty} K_n(\tau_1, \ldots, \tau_p, \xi_{p+1}, \ldots, \xi_n)\kappa_0'(t - \xi_{p+1})$$

$$\cdots \kappa_0'(t - \xi_n)\, d\xi_{p+1} \cdots d\xi_n. \tag{11.3}$$

The expansion (11.2) in terms of $\Delta\kappa = \kappa - \kappa_0$ may be convergent for histories κ for which the original expansion (6.1) is not convergent. The expression (11.2) then provides an analytic continuation of the original expression for the constitutive functional. In Sections 12 and 13 we consider two specific examples of relations of the type (11.2).

12. Small Motions Superposed on Stress-Relaxation at Constant Deformation

The response $R(\kappa_0, t)$ to a step-function shear history $\kappa_0(\tau) = \kappa_0 H(\tau)$ was discussed in Section 5. Let us suppose that an additional time-dependent shear $\Delta\kappa(\tau)$ is superposed on the base history $\kappa_0(\tau)$:

$$\kappa(\tau) = \kappa_0 H(\tau) + \Delta\kappa(\tau). \tag{12.1}$$

Then (11.2) yields

$$\sigma(t) = \sum_{p=0}^{\infty} \int_0^{\infty} \cdots \int_0^{\infty} R_p(\kappa_0, t; \tau_1, \ldots, \tau_p) \Delta\kappa'(t - \tau_1) \cdots \Delta\kappa'(t - \tau_p)$$

$$\times d\tau_1 \cdots d\tau_p, \tag{12.2}$$

where, from (11.3),

$$R_p(\kappa_0, t; \tau_1, \ldots, \tau_p) = \sum_{n\,\text{odd}} \binom{n}{p} K_n(\tau_1, \ldots, \tau_p, t, \ldots, t)\kappa_0^{n-p}. \tag{12.3}$$

Constitutive equations of the type (12.2) have been discussed by Appleby and Lee.[29]

Approximations to (12.2) such as those considered in Sections 7–9 can now be obtained. For example, if $\Delta\kappa'$ is small at all times, it may be possible to omit all except a few low-order integrals, e.g.,

$$\sigma(t) = R_0(\kappa_0, t) + \int_0^\infty R_1(\kappa_0, t; \tau)\,\Delta\kappa'(t - \tau)\,d\tau + \cdots. \qquad (12.4)$$

We note from (12.3) that

$$pR_p(\kappa_0, t; \tau_1, \ldots, \tau_{p-1}, t) = (\partial/\partial\kappa_0)R_{p-1}(\kappa_0, t; \tau_1, \ldots, \tau_{p-1}), \qquad (12.5)$$

and in particular that

$$R_1(\kappa_0, t; t) = (\partial/\partial\kappa_0)R_0(\kappa_0, t). \qquad (12.6)$$

A consistency relation similar to (12.6) has been noticed by Pipkin and Rivlin.[30] Such relations are useful in providing estimates of higher-order terms when no experimental data are available.

13. Small Motions Superposed on Steady Shearing Motion

The stress $\sigma = \gamma\eta(\gamma^2)$ in a steady shearing motion at the rate $\kappa_0'(\tau) = \gamma$ was discussed in Section 5. The apparent viscosity $\eta(\gamma^2)$ is given in terms of the kernels K_n by (6.4), and in terms of the Rivlin–Ericksen coefficients (Section 9) by

$$\eta(\gamma^2) = \mu(1 + \gamma^2 a_{111} + \gamma^4 a_{11111} + \cdots). \qquad (13.1)$$

If an additional time-dependent shear $\Delta\kappa(\tau)$ is superposed on the base history $\kappa_0(\tau) = \gamma\tau$, so that

$$\kappa(\tau) = \gamma\tau + \Delta\kappa(\tau), \qquad (13.2)$$

then (11.2) yields

$$\sigma(t) = \sum_{p=0}^\infty \int_0^\infty \cdots \int_0^\infty \varphi_p(\gamma; \tau_1, \ldots, \tau_p)\,\Delta\kappa'(t - \tau_1) \cdots \Delta\kappa'(t - \tau_p)$$

$$d\tau_1 \cdots d\tau_p, \qquad (13.3)$$

where, from (11.3),

$$\varphi_p(\gamma; \tau_1, \ldots, \tau_p) = \sum_{n\,\text{odd}} \binom{n}{p} \gamma^{n-p} \int_0^\infty \cdots \int_0^\infty K_n(\tau_1, \ldots, \tau_p,$$

$$\xi_{p+1}, \ldots, \xi_n)\,d\xi_{p+1} \cdots d\xi_n. \qquad (13.4)$$

In particular, $\varphi_0 = \gamma\eta(\gamma^2)$.

Approximations to (13.3) can now be considered, and the relation (10.16) is one such approximation. Another, valid for small motions $\Delta\kappa$, is

$$\sigma(t) = \gamma\eta(\gamma^2) + \int_0^\infty \varphi_1(\gamma;\tau)\,\Delta\kappa'(t-\tau)\,d\tau + \cdots, \tag{13.5}$$

where φ_1 is an even function of γ.

From (13.4) we obtain the consistency relations

$$(\partial/\partial\gamma)\varphi_{p-1}(\gamma;\tau_1,\ldots,\tau_{p-1}) = p\int_0^\infty \varphi_p(\gamma;\tau_1,\ldots,\tau_p)\,d\tau_p, \tag{13.6}$$

and in particular

$$(d/d\gamma)[\gamma\eta(\gamma^2)] = \int_0^\infty \varphi_1(\gamma;\tau)\,d\tau. \tag{13.7}$$

Three-dimensional forms of approximations of the type (13.5) have been discussed by Owen and Pipkin.[32]

14. Some Remarks on Perturbation Methods

First-order approximations can formally be regarded as obtained by setting some parameter equal to zero, as for example the dimensionless duration t/T in Section 8, or the typical shear A/L or the unsteadiness parameter ωT in Section 10. Once a parameter has been set equal to zero, it no longer appears in the equation. With the parameter no longer in evidence, it is possible to forget that smallness of the parameter is required for validity of the equation. Such forgetfulness can lead to inaccurate results, but absurdities based on the fact that the parameter is large cannot occur in a solution which does not contain that parameter. For this reason, first-order approximations usually have the self-consistency desired in the definition of an idealized material.

These remarks have more point, by contrast, when second- or higher-order approximations are considered. In a second-order approximation, the perturbation parameter is still present, even if it is not made explicit, and one can usually obtain absurd results by applying the equation to flows in which the second-order term is as large or larger than the first-order term.

For example, the second-order approximation (8.4) for short motions predicts that with a step-function shear history $\kappa H(\tau)$, the stress becomes negative when t is greater than $|F_0/F_1|$ (assuming that $F_1 < 0$). This absurd result clearly indicates that the equation can be valid only when tF_1/F_0 is small.

As another example, let us consider a slow-motion approximation to the steady shearing equation $\sigma = \gamma\eta(\gamma^2)$. Positive energy dissipation requires that $\eta(\gamma^2) > 0$ if $\gamma \neq 0$. Let us apply this restriction to the approximation $\eta(\gamma^2) = \eta(0) + \eta'(0)\gamma^2 + O(\gamma^4)$. From $\eta(\gamma^2) > 0$ we conclude that $\eta(0) \geqslant 0$, and if $\eta(0) > 0$ then nothing whatever can be said about the sign of $\eta'(0)$. However, let us treat the second-order approximation $\eta(\gamma^2) = \eta(0) + \eta'(0)\gamma^2$ as if it were exact. We can then conclude that $\eta'(0) \geqslant 0$. This particular type of unwarranted conclusion, based on treatment of approximations as if they were exact, has occurred repeatedly in the literature.

Coleman et al.[31] have pointed out an interesting absurdity which arises when the following particular slow-motion approximation is treated as if it were exact, with no $O(\varepsilon^2)$ term (see (10.14)):

$$\sigma = \mu[u_y - \varepsilon|b_2|u_{yt} + O(\varepsilon^2)]. \tag{14.1}$$

Here we use dimensionless variables as defined in (10.2), but with a typical length L which will represent the width of a channel containing the fluid, and with ω then defined by (10.3). With (14.1), the dimensionless momentum equation becomes

$$u_t = u_{yy} - \varepsilon|b_2|u_{yyt} + O(\varepsilon^2). \tag{14.2}$$

To study the stability of the state of rest in the channel, we follow Coleman et al.[31] in considering an initial-value problem with $u'(y', 0) = A\sin(n\pi y'/L)$ in terms of dimensional variables, where the disturbance amplitude A is to be arbitrarily small. A solution of (14.2) satisfying this initial condition and the (dimensionless) boundary conditions $u(0, t) = u(1, t) = 0$ is given by

$$u(y, t) = \sin(n\pi y)\exp[\lambda t], \tag{14.3}$$

where λ satisfies

$$\lambda = -(n\pi)^2 + \varepsilon|b_2|(n\pi)^2\lambda + O(\varepsilon^2). \tag{14.4}$$

Then,

$$\lambda = -(n\pi)^2 - \varepsilon|b_2|(n\pi)^4 + O(\varepsilon^2). \tag{14.5}$$

The $O(\varepsilon)$ term has a stabilizing influence, since it makes λ more negative than it otherwise would be. But now let us omit the $O(\varepsilon^2)$ term in all equations, and treat the resulting equations as if they were exact. From (14.4) we would obtain the result

$$\lambda = (n\pi)^2/[\varepsilon|b_2|(n\pi)^2 - 1]. \tag{14.6}$$

Then, for sufficiently large n, λ is positive, and an initial disturbance of arbitrarily small amplitude will grow without bound. One might conclude that the state of rest is unstable. However, in the formally unstable modes, the second-order term $\varepsilon|b_2|u_{yt}$ is larger than the first-order term u_y, and there is no reason to expect that (14.1) has any bearing on the problem.

15. Conclusion

Constitutive equations of simple useful forms should not be expected to provide accurate descriptions of the behavior of fluids over the full range of flow conditions implied in the term *viscoelastic*. The physical properties of most direct importance in a given type of flow may have little or no bearing on the behavior of the material under other conditions. One fluid may be described under various circumstances by many different narrow-range approximations. If a simple narrow-range approximation is required in order to make solution of a problem feasible, then the particular approximation to be used should be determined in the course of solving the problem. There is no reason to believe that an approximation valid in one type of motion will also be valid in other types, and there is no reason to require that every narrow-range approximation should exhibit the self-consistency desired in the definition of an idealized material.

REFERENCES

1. R. S. Rivlin, Viscoelastic fluids, *in* "Research Frontiers in Fluid Dynamics" (R. J. Seeger and G. Temple, eds.). Wiley (Interscience), New York, 1965.
2. A. E. Green and R. S. Rivlin, Mechanics of nonlinear materials with memory, *Arch. Rational Mech. Anal.* **1**, 1 (1957).
3. W. Noll, A mathematical theory of the mechanical behavior of continuous media, *Arch. Rational Mech. Anal.* **2**, 197 (1958).
4. A. E. Green, R. S. Rivlin, and A. J. M. Spencer, Mechanics of nonlinear materials with memory II, *Arch. Rational Mech. Anal.* **3**, 82 (1959).
5. A. S. Wineman and A. C. Pipkin, Material symmetry restrictions on constitutive equations, *Arch. Rational Mech. Anal.* **17**, 184 (1964).
6. R. S. Rivlin, Consitutive equations for certain classes of deformations, *Arch. Rational Mech. Anal.* **3**, 304 (1959).
7. R. S. Rivlin, Solution of some problems in the exact theory of viscoelasticity, *J. Rational Mech. Anal.* **5**, 179 (1956).
8. W. O. Criminale, Jr., J. L. Ericksen, and G. L. Filbey, Jr., Steady shear flow of non-Newtonian fluids, *Arch. Rational Mech. Anal.* **1**, 410 (1958).
9. J. L. Ericksen, Behavior of certain viscoelastic materials in laminar shearing motions, *in* "Viscoelasticity: Phenomenological Aspects" (J. T. Bergen, ed.). Academic Press, New York, 1960.

10. B. D. Coleman and W. Noll, On certain steady flows in general fluids, *Arch. Rational Mech. Anal.* **3**, 289 (1959).
11. R. S. Rivlin, Stress-relaxation in incompressible elastic materials at constant deformation, *Quart. Appl. Math.* **14**, 83 (1956).
12. B. D. Coleman and W. Noll, Foundations of linear viscoelasticity, *Rev. Modern Phys.* **33**, 239 (1961).
13. E. H. Lee, Viscoelastic stress analysis, *in* "Structural Mechanics" (J. N. Goodier and N. J. Hoff, eds.). Pergamon, Oxford, 1960.
14. E. H. Lee and I. Kanter, Wave propagation in finite rods of viscoelastic material, *J. Appl. Phys.* **24**, 1115 (1953).
15. B. D. Coleman, Thermodynamics of materials with memory, *Arch. Rational Mech. Anal.* **17**, 1 (1964).
16. A. E. Green and J. E. Adkins, "Large Elastic Deformations." Oxford Univ. Press, London and New York, 1960.
17. N. C. Huang and E. H. Lee, Nonlinear Viscoelasticity for Short Time Ranges, Stanford Univ., Div. of Eng. Mech., Stanford, California, Tech. Rept. 151 (November 1964).
18. E. Varley, Acceleration fronts in viscoelastic materials, *Arch. Rational Mech. Anal.* **19**, 215 (1965).
19. B. D. Coleman, M. E. Gurtin, and I. Herrera R., Waves in materials with memory I, *Arch. Rational Mech. Anal.* **19**, 1 (1965).
20. B. D. Coleman and M. E. Gurtin, Waves in materials with memory II, *Arch. Rational Mech. Anal.* **19**, 239 (1965).
21. R. S. Rivlin and J. L. Ericksen, Stress-deformation relations for isotropic materials, *J. Rational Mech. Anal.* **4**, 323 (1955).
22. A. Erdelyi, "Asymptotic Expansions." Dover, New York, 1956.
23. P. P. Niiler and A. C. Pipkin, Finite amplitude shear waves in some non-Newtonian fluids, *Intern. J. Eng. Sci.* **2**, 305 (1964).
24. B. D. Coleman and W. Noll, An approximation theorem for functionals, *Arch. Rational Mech. Anal.* **6**, 355 (1960).
25. W. E. Langlois and R. S. Rivlin, Slow steady-state flow of viscoelastic fluids through non-circular tubes, *Rend. Mat.* **22**, 169 (1963).
26. B. Caswell and W. H. Schwartz, Creeping motion of a non-Newtonian fluid past a sphere, *J. Fluid Mech.* **13**, 417 (1962).
27. H. Giezekus, Some secondary flow phenomena in general viscoelastic fluids, *Proc. Fourth Intern. Congr. Rheology, Part I* (E. H. Lee, ed.), Wiley (Interscience), New York, 1965.
28. H. Markovitz and B. D. Coleman, Incompressible second-order fluids, *Advan. Appl. Mech.* **8**, 69ff (1964).
29. E. J. Appleby and E. H. Lee, Superposed deformations in nonlinear viscoelasticity, Stanford Univ., Div. Eng. Mech., Stanford, California, Tech. Rept. 149 (June, 1964).
30. A. C. Pipkin and R. S. Rivlin, Small deformations superposed on large deformations in materials with fading memory, *Arch. Rational Mech. Anal.* **8**, 297 (1961).
31. B. D. Coleman, R. J. Duffin, and V. J. Mizel, Instability, uniqueness, and nonexistence theorems for the equation $u_t = u_{xx} - u_{xtx}$ on a strip, *Arch. Rational Mech. Anal.* **19**, 100 (1965).
32. D. R. Owen and A. C. Pipkin, Nearly viscometric flows, Brown Univ., Div. of Apld. Math., Providence, Rhode Island (May, 1966).

Remarks on Compatibility†

R. L. FOSDICK

Department of Mechanics
Illinois Institute of Technology
Chicago, Illinois

1. Introduction

Within the context of finite elasticity theory, Ericksen,[3] in 1954 considered a rational approach to determining deformations possible in every isotropic, incompressible, elastic material which can be placed in equilibrium in the absence of body forces. His analysis led not only to all of the known solutions at that time but also to the discovery of three new solutions. In a later publication[8] Ericksen extended his work to include compressible elastic materials. In this case the problem was much less difficult and the class of solutions considerably more restrictive to include only those deformations which are homogeneous. This result was due, essentially, to the absence of the arbitrary hydrostatic pressure term which accounts for additional flexibility in determining solutions for media which are incompressible.

In Ericksen's earlier work on incompressible bodies he conjectured that deformations which possess constant principal strain invariants must necessarily be homogeneous, and, therefore, did not search for deformations of this class which were otherwise. In the present paper we shall construct a counterexample (see (5.7)) to this conjecture. In so doing we raise the question of whether or not new exact solutions of the constant strain invariant type exist. The counterexample obtained here is not a new solution and, in fact, can be found in Ericksen's work buried within a five parameter set of solutions whose strain invariants are not generally constant. However, it has led to the recent construction of a new exact solution by Singh and Pipkin,[4]‡ and, therefore, has affirmatively served its intended purpose. The unanswered question

† This research was supported in part by the National Science Foundation.

‡ Based on the deformation field (5.7) Singh and Pipkin[4] have recently found a new exact solution of this class. Their deformation field is of the form $r = vR$, $\theta = \alpha \log R + \beta\Theta$, $z = \eta Z$, where v, α, β, η are constants. For incompressibility, v, β, η again must satisfy (4.39).

which remains is "do other exact solutions of the constant strain invariant class exist?" The answer to this question is the subject of current investigation.

In Section 2 we summarize some known results concerning the kinematics of deformation. In particular, we review the conditions of compatibility. In geometric language these conditions correspond to the vanishing of the Riemann (curvature) tensor which is calculated with either the right Cauchy–Green strain tensor or the inverse of the left Cauchy–Green strain tensor considered as metric. Further, the Ricci and the Einstein tensors, which are noted in Section 3 to possess a significant relationship to compatibility, are introduced.

The problem of determining a deformation from information concerning the strain will usually involve conditions of compatibility. Since the present form of these conditions are rather difficult to apply, in Section 3 we shall present some equivalent expressions which appear to possess certain advantages. These advantages should emerge not only in the application of compatibility to specific problems, but also in more fundamental questions concerning the compatibility conditions, such as their redundancy or their variational characterization.

In Section 4, we recall Ericksen's conjecture and formulate a kinematic approach, based on compatibility, which can be used to determine deformations with constant strain invariants. A form of the compatibility conditions which is obtained in Section 3 is seen to be particularly convenient for this problem. We treat in detail some aspects of the case of two equal principal strains, and obtain a three-parameter set of deformations which are not homogeneous but which possess constant principal strain invariants. The deformations are noted to retain these characteristics when they are trivially extended to a four parameter set whose principle strains are distinct.

Finally, in Section 5 we investigate the equilibrium of an isotropic incompressible elastic material in the absence of body forces with regard to the deformations with constant strain invariants which are obtained in Section 4. We find that certain deformations (see (5.7)) selected from those found in Section 4 (see (4.38)) do indeed satisfy the requirements imposed by equilibrium and, therefore, serve as a counterexample to Ericksen's conjecture.

2. Kinematic Concepts and Notation

The underlying frame of reference to be employed throughout most of this paper is a fixed system of rectangular Cartesian coordinates.

Only in the latter part of Section 4 and in Section 5 do we, for convenience, introduce a system of cylindrical coordinates. Vectors **u**, tensors **A**, and points **X** will be denoted by bold face letters and their Cartesian components will be written u_i, $A_{ij...k}$, and X_i respectively. If **A** denotes a second order tensor then $\mathbf{A}^T$, $\mathbf{A}^{-1}$, det **A**, and tr **A** represent its transpose, inverse, determinant, and trace, respectively. Finally, the usual summation convention over repeated indices is to be assumed.

The deformation of a continuous media is a one-to-one mapping of the position **X** of each material point relative to some reference configuration into its respective position **x** in space as time t progresses. This is expressed as

$$\mathbf{x} = \mathbf{x}(\mathbf{X}, t). \tag{2.1}$$

The deformation gradient for each material point at time t is defined as the nonsingular tensor **F** with Cartesian components[†]

$$F_{ij} \overset{\text{def}}{=} \frac{\partial}{\partial X_j} x_i(\mathbf{X}, t) = x_{i,j}. \tag{2.2}$$

Two strain measures which are often employed in continuum mechanics are the right Cauchy–Green tensor **C** and the inverse of the left Cauchy–Green tensor **c** defined respectively in terms of **F** by

$$\mathbf{C} = \mathbf{F}^T\mathbf{F}, \qquad \mathbf{c} = (\mathbf{F}^{-1})^T\mathbf{F}^{-1}. \tag{2.3}$$

The Cartesian components of these tensors are given by[‡]

$$C_{ij} = \frac{\partial x_m}{\partial X_i}\frac{\partial x_m}{\partial X_j}, \tag{2.4}$$

and

$$c_{ij} = \frac{\partial X_m}{\partial x_i}\frac{\partial X_m}{\partial x_j}. \tag{2.5}$$

It is well known that in order that there exist a deformation which satisfies either (2.4) or (2.5) for a given strain field, **C** or **c**, then certain integration conditions must be satisfied by the strain. These so-called compatibility conditions are usually[§] given in the form

---

[†] A subscripted comma followed by an index is used as a shorthand notation for partial differentiation with respect to the rectangular Cartesian coordinates **X**. Also, explicit functional dependence on time t will be surpressed in all but the last section of this paper where it is, in fact, irrelevant since equilibrium will be considered there.

[‡] We use the notation $X_m = X_m(\mathbf{x}, t)$ to represent the inverse of Eq. (2.1).

[§] See, e.g., Truesdell and Toupin,[1] Section 34.

$$^{(C)}\mathbf{R} = 0 \quad \text{and} \quad ^{(c)}\mathbf{R} = 0, \tag{2.6}$$

where, e.g., $^{(C)}\mathbf{R}$ denotes the Riemann tensor often encountered in general tensor analysis and calculated here with $\mathbf{C}$ considered as metric. The Riemann tensor possesses the representation†

$$^{(C)}R_{skrl} = \Gamma_{kls,r} - \Gamma_{krs,l} - [\Gamma^p_{kl}\Gamma_{srp} - \Gamma^p_{kr}\Gamma_{slp}], \tag{2.7}$$

where we have employed the following notational definitions:

$$\Gamma_{kls} \overset{\text{def}}{=} \tfrac{1}{2}(C_{ks,l} + C_{ls,k} - C_{kl,s}), \tag{2.8}$$

$$\Gamma^p_{kl} \overset{\text{def}}{=} C^{-1}_{pm}\Gamma_{klm}. \tag{2.9}$$

Although there are 81 components of the Riemann tensor (2.7) all but 6 are trivially zero as can be concluded from its following general properties:

$$^{(C)}R_{skrl} = -\,^{(C)}R_{ksrl}$$

$$= -\,^{(C)}R_{sklr} \tag{2.10}$$

$$= \,^{(C)}R_{rlsk},$$

$$^{(C)}R_{skrl} + \,^{(C)}R_{srlk} + \,^{(C)}R_{slkr} = 0.$$

Clearly, equations analogous to (2.7)–(2.10) can also be written for $^{(c)}\mathbf{R}$ but we shall not do so here. We merely remark that in this case the results may be formally obtained by replacing $\mathbf{C}$ by $\mathbf{c}$ and $\mathbf{X}$ by $\mathbf{x}$.

Throughout the remainder of the present and the next section of this paper we shall be concerned with the right Cauchy–Green tensor $\mathbf{C}$ and its related compatibility equations. Our immediate aim is to establish an appropriate notation and to review some known and relevant results. It is clear that analogous treatment could be applied to the strain tensor $\mathbf{c}$.

It is convenient to define the Cartesian components of associated

---

† The notation employed in (2.7)–(2.9) is designed so as to correspond to certain results from general tensor analysis. For example, (2.8) corresponds to the Christoffel symbol of the first kind with $\mathbf{C}$ considered as the metric while (2.9) is analogous to the Christoffel symbol of the second kind. The position of the index as a superscript is to be considered only as a distinguishing mark and has no hidden tensor connotations. It has been used solely for notational convenience and is subject to the usual summation convention.

tensor fields through, for example, the relations

$$V^k_{\;l} \overset{\text{def}}{=} C^{-1}_{km} V_{ml}, \tag{2.11}$$

or

$$V^{kl} \overset{\text{def}}{=} C^{-1}_{km} C^{-1}_{lr} V_{mr}, \tag{2.12}$$

where V_{ml} are the components of the given field and $V^k_{\;l}$ and V^{kl} are the components of the associated fields. It follows that C^{-1}_{kl} are actually the components of an associated tensor field which we shall alternatively define through

$$C^{kl} \overset{\text{def}}{=} C^{-1}_{kl} = C^{-1}_{km} C^{-1}_{lr} C_{mr}. \tag{2.13}$$

The notation C^{kl} will be employed in place of C^{-1}_{kl} whenever it appears most useful to do so. It also appears advantageous to draw upon the concept of covariant differentiation from general tensor analysis and define the operation "$\|$" through, for example,

$$V^k_{\;l}\|_m \overset{\text{def}}{=} V^k_{\;l,m} + \Gamma^k_{pm} V^p_{\;l} - \Gamma^p_{lm} V^k_{\;p}, \tag{2.14}$$

or

$$V^{kl}\|_m \overset{\text{def}}{=} V^{kl}_{,m} + \Gamma^k_{pm} V^{pl} + \Gamma^l_{pm} V^{kp}. \tag{2.15}$$

It is now clear that the so-called Ricci identities of tensor analysis hold:

$$C_{kl}\|_m = C^{kl}\|_m = 0. \tag{2.16}$$

Finally, if e_{klm} is to denote the components of the usual alternator tensor, then we shall define the permutation symbols ε_{klm} and ε^{klm} through

$$\varepsilon_{klm} \overset{\text{def}}{=} e_{klm}\sqrt{\det \mathbf{C}},$$

$$\varepsilon^{klm} \overset{\text{def}}{=} e_{klm}/\sqrt{\det \mathbf{C}}. \tag{2.17}$$

The vanishing of the Riemann tensor has long been connected to the conditions of compatibility in continuum mechanics. In Section 3 we shall see that the Ricci and Einstein tensors play an equally important role in establishing the requirements of compatibility. Hence a word about their structure seems appropriate. The Ricci tensor is defined through the following associated form of the Riemann tensor:

$$^{(C)}R^m_{krl} \overset{\text{def}}{=} C^{ms}\, {}^{(C)}R_{skrl}. \tag{2.18}$$

From (2.18) the Ricci tensor $\mathbf{R}$ is given by

$$R_{kr} \overset{\text{def}}{=} {}^{(C)}R^m_{krm}, \tag{2.19}$$

which by (2.10) is symmetric. It is not difficult to show with the aid of (2.7), (2.9), and (2.18) that

$$R_{kr} = [\log \sqrt{\det \mathbf{C}}]_{,kr} - \Gamma^m_{kr,m} + \Gamma^q_{km}\Gamma^m_{qr} - \Gamma^q_{kr}[\log \sqrt{\det \mathbf{C}}]_{,q}. \tag{2.20}$$

It can be shown that ${}^{(C)}\mathbf{R}$ given in (2.7) satisfies the Bianchi identities

$$ {}^{(C)}R_{mkrl}\|_q + {}^{(C)}R_{mklq}\|_r + {}^{(C)}R_{mkqr}\|_l = 0. \tag{2.21}$$

Multiplying (2.21) through by $C^{ml}C^{kr}C^{qp}$ it readily follows with the aid of (2.10), (2.13), (2.16), (2.18), and (2.19) that

$$(R^{rp} - \tfrac{1}{2}RC^{rp})\|_r = 0, \tag{2.22}$$

where R^{rp} represents the components of an associated form of $\mathbf{R}$ and where R is defined by

$$R \overset{\text{def}}{=} C^{mr}R_{mr}. \tag{2.23}$$

The expression in parentheses in (2.22) represents the components of an associated form of what is commonly known as the Einstein tensor $\mathbf{E}$ in tensor analysis. Thus,

$$E_{kl} \overset{\text{def}}{=} R_{kl} - \tfrac{1}{2}RC_{kl}, \tag{2.24}$$

and (2.22) becomes

$$E^{kl}\|_l = 0. \tag{2.25}$$

The inversion of (2.24) can be easily carried out to obtain

$$R_{kr} = E_{kr} - EC_{kr}, \tag{2.26}$$

where

$$E \overset{\text{def}}{=} C^{mr}E_{mr}. \tag{2.27}$$

3. Other Forms of Compatibility

The compatibility equations (2.6) and (2.7) are in a form which is in general difficult to apply. One reason for this is because Eqs. (2.6) express 81 conditions of which all but 6 are trivial identities. It would be advantageous to express the 6 nontrivial equations of compatibility as the vanishing of a simpler, second-order symmetric tensor and thus to preserve the tensor character of compatibility while reducing the conditions to just what is essential. This is possible in a number of ways, one of which demonstrates the equivalence of the Riemann (2.7), the Ricci (2.20), and the Einstein (2.24) tensors.

The main theorem which relates the Riemann, the Ricci, and the Einstein tensors is provided by

THEOREM 3.1. *The Riemann tensor $^{(C)}\mathbf{R}$ and the Einstein tensor $\mathbf{E}$ are related by*

$$^{(C)}R_{skrl} = \varepsilon_{skm}\varepsilon_{rlp}E^{mp}. \tag{3.1}$$

This theorem does not appear to have been previously recognized applicable in continuum mechanics, however, it is indeed a known result in the context of differential geometry for three dimensional space. Therefore, we shall not include its proof here.

Theorem 3.1 makes possible the following equivalent representations of compatibility:

THEOREM 3.2. *Any one of the following three statements is equivalent to the remaining two:*
 (a) *The Riemann tensor vanishes,* $^{(C)}\mathbf{R} = 0$.
 (b) *The Ricci tensor vanishes,* $\mathbf{R} = 0$.
 (c) *The Einstein tensor vanishes,* $\mathbf{E} = 0$.

Proof. The proof of this theorem follows from (3.1), the inverted form of (3.1)

$$E^{np} = \tfrac{1}{4}\varepsilon^{skn}\varepsilon^{rlp}\,^{(C)}R_{skrl}, \tag{3.2}$$

(2.24), and (2.26). For example, if $\mathbf{E}$ vanishes then (2.26) implies that $\mathbf{R}$ must also vanish, while (3.1) yields the vanishing of $^{(C)}\mathbf{R}$. The remaining combinations are treated similarly.

We have just shown that the six equations of compatibility may be expressed as the vanishing of either the Ricci tensor $\mathbf{R}$ or the Einstein tensor $\mathbf{E}$. The fact that these six equations are not all independent follows from the restriction that the Bianchi identities (2.21) place on the Riemann tensor. Now, however, these restrictions take the particularly convenient form (2.25). Therefore, it should be possible to treat their implication with regard to solution of the compatibility equations analogous to the manner in which Washizu[2] has handled the simpler linear problem.

Further, we remark that the Ricci tensor represented by (2.20) simplifies considerably in the case when $\det \mathbf{C}$ is constant.† Thus, the compatibility equations for this situation become

$$\Gamma^q_{km}\Gamma^m_{qr} - \Gamma^m_{kr,m} = 0. \tag{3.3}$$

In Section 4 we shall consider deformations which possess constant strain invariants for which (3.3) will also serve as an appropriate expression of compatibility.

We shall conclude this section with the following theorem which demonstrates another representation for the equations of compatibility.

THEOREM 3.3. *Let A_{sl} represent the Cartesian components of an arbitrary nonsingular symmetric tensor $\mathbf{A}$, and define the symmetric tensor $\mathcal{R}$ through*

$$\mathcal{R}_{kr} \overset{\text{def}}{=} {}^{(C)}R_{skrl}A_{sl}. \tag{3.4}$$

Then ${}^{(C)}\mathbf{R}$ vanishes if and only if $\mathcal{R}$ vanishes.

Proof. Clearly, if ${}^{(C)}\mathbf{R}$ vanishes it follows from (3.4) that $\mathcal{R}$ must also vanish. Hence in order to prove the theorem it remains to show the converse. This will be established once (3.4) is solved for ${}^{(C)}\mathbf{R}$ in terms of $\mathcal{R}$. To this end recall (3.1) and substitute into (3.4) to obtain

$$\mathcal{R}_{kr} = \varepsilon_{skm}\varepsilon_{rln}E^{mn}A_{sl},$$

which by (2.17) may be written

$$\mathcal{R}_{kr} = (\det \mathbf{C})e_{skm}e_{rln}E^{mn}A_{sl}. \tag{3.5}$$

From the theory of determinants it follows that

$$e_{skm}\det \mathbf{A}^{-1} = e_{pqt}A^{-1}_{ps}A^{-1}_{qk}A^{-1}_{tm},$$

where the inverse $\mathbf{A}^{-1}$ exists by hypothesis. After multiplication of this result through by $e_{rln}A_{sl}$ and substitution into (3.5) we reach

$$\mathcal{R}_{kr} = (\det \mathbf{C})(\det \mathbf{A})(A^{-1}_{nk}A^{-1}_{rm} - A^{-1}_{rk}A^{-1}_{nm})E^{mn}. \tag{3.6}$$

Now, since (3.1) already represents ${}^{(C)}\mathbf{R}$ in terms of $\mathbf{E}$, inversion of (3.6) to obtain $\mathbf{E}$ in terms of $\mathcal{R}$ will result in the final inversion sought. To invert (3.6) we first use the symmetry of $\mathbf{A}$ and form the products

$$\mathcal{R}_{kr}A_{rq} = (\det \mathbf{C})(\det \mathbf{A})(A^{-1}_{nk}E^{qn} - \delta_{qk}A^{-1}_{nm}E^{mn}),$$

† For example, $\det \mathbf{C} = 1$ for an incompressible material.

and

$$\mathcal{R}_{kr}A_{rk} = -2(\det \mathbf{C})(\det \mathbf{A})A_{nm}^{-1}E^{mn}.$$

Then substitution of the latter result into the former produces

$$(\det \mathbf{C})(\det \mathbf{A})A_{nk}^{-1}E^{qn} = \mathcal{R}_{kr}A_{rq} - \tfrac{1}{2}\delta_{qk}\mathcal{R}_{nm}A_{mn},$$

which when multiplied through by A_{kp} yields the inverted form

$$E^{qp} = (\det \mathbf{C})^{-1}(\det \mathbf{A})^{-1}(A_{kp}\mathcal{R}_{kr}A_{rq} - \tfrac{1}{2}A_{qp}\mathcal{R}_{nm}A_{mn}). \tag{3.7}$$

From (3.7) it evidently follows that if $\mathcal{R}$ vanishes then $\mathbf{E}$ must also vanish, and this fact in addition to Theorem 3.2 completes the proof of this theorem.

Clearly, many choices of $\mathbf{A}$ are possible in Theorem 3.3. The overriding criterion for selecting a particular $\mathbf{A}$ is the desire to express the compatibility conditions in the simplest and most convenient form. We do not attempt to discuss this problem of a particular choice any further here except to mention that for the choice $A_{sl} \overset{\text{def}}{=} C_{sl}^{-1}$, $\mathcal{R}$ becomes the Ricci tensor $\mathbf{R}$ and the theorem becomes identical to the statement (b) of Theorem 3.2.

4. Deformations with Constant Strain Invariants

The problem of determining the class of deformation fields, in continuum mechanics which possess constant strain invariants is basically a problem of kinematics. If, however, it is also required that the deformations are to be such that a particular body characterized by a given constitutive equation is to be in equilibrium in the absence of body force, the set of possible deformations will generally be further limited.

In 1954 Ericksen[3] investigated the class of deformations which are possible in *every* isotropic, incompressible, elastic body which can be placed in equilibrium with zero body force density.† In the case when the three principal strain invariants are constant Ericksen conjectured that the most general possible deformation is homogeneous; i.e., of the form $\mathbf{x} = \mathbf{A} \cdot \mathbf{X} + \mathbf{b}$ where $\mathbf{A}$ is a constant nonsingular matrix and where $\mathbf{b}$ is a constant vector. It is not clear from the context whether Ericksen's conjecture is supposed to be interpreted in a strictly kinematic sense in which case it would imply that deformations which are other than homogeneous and which possess constant strain invariants are nonexistent, or whether the (nonexistent) deformations are also supposed

† Solutions of this type will be termed "exact" in the sequel.

to be in equilibrium in an elastic, isotropic incompressible body in the absence of body forces. In any case it is possible to exhibit a counter-example which invalidates the conjecture and which, therefore, suggests that new exact solutions in incompressible finite elasticity theory can be constructed.[†] We remark that since the principal strain invariants are defined by

$$I \overset{def}{=} \operatorname{tr} \mathbf{C}, \qquad II \overset{def}{=} \tfrac{1}{2}[(\operatorname{tr} \mathbf{C})^2 - \operatorname{tr} \mathbf{C}^2], \qquad III \overset{def}{=} \det \mathbf{C}, \qquad (4.1)$$

where $\mathbf{C}$ is given by (2.3), it is clear that for homogeneous deformations the invariants are constant. However, based on a known, although not often referenced, theorem due to Michal[5] which asserts that a deformation is homogeneous if and only if the right Cauchy–Green strain tensor $\mathbf{C}$ is constant, the converse appears questionable. It was Michal's theorem which initially cast doubt on Ericksen's conjecture.

Although the main result in the remainder of this paper is a counter-example to Ericksen's conjecture, which can be presented immediately, we prefer to deduce it so as to exhibit a possible method of approach to finding all deformations with constant strain invariants by way of a particular example. Thus, in this section we formulate the general *kinematics problem* associated with determining the complete class of constant strain invariant deformations and treat in detail an aspect of the case of two equal principal strains.[‡] It is found that besides the homogeneous deformation, deformations which transform a sector of a hollow circular cylinder into a sector of another hollow circular cylinder and deformations which transform conical shaped bodies of revolution into other such shaped bodies are also of the constant strain invariant type. These results are extended to the case where all three principal strains are unequal. We remark that certain assumptions which are employed rules out any claim of completeness.

The general procedure is to integrate the strain-deformation equations (2.4) subject to the condition that the three invariants defined in (4.1) are constant. The restrictions on $\mathbf{C}$ which imply that integration of (2.4) is possible are expressed in the equations of compatibility (2.6). The form of the compatibility conditions which are particularly convenient here consist in the vanishing of the Ricci tensor (2.20), since under the hypothesis that the strain invariants are constant these conditions reduce to the more tractable form (3.3).

The characteristic equation for the strain tensor $\mathbf{C}$ shows that if its

---

[†] In fact, Singh and Pipkin[4] have recently constructed a new exact solution based on the counterexample presented here. See footnote (‡) on page 109.

[‡] In Section 5 we shall take up the question of equilibrium.

three principal invariants are assumed constant throughout any deformed media then its principal strains $(\lambda_1, \lambda_2, \lambda_3)$ must also be constant. It is clear that this basic hypothesis is not sufficient to place any restriction on the pointwise variation of the principal directions of **C**. Thus, **C** admits the representation

$$\mathbf{C} = \mathbf{Q}\boldsymbol{\Lambda}\mathbf{Q}^T, \tag{4.2}$$

where $\boldsymbol{\Lambda}$ denotes the constant diagonal matrix

$$\boldsymbol{\Lambda} = \begin{Vmatrix} \lambda_1 & 0 & 0 \\ 0 & \lambda_2 & 0 \\ 0 & 0 & \lambda_3 \end{Vmatrix} \tag{4.3}$$

and where $\mathbf{Q(X)}$ is an arbitrary position dependent orthogonal tensor,

$$\mathbf{Q}\mathbf{Q}^T = \mathbf{Q}^T\mathbf{Q}$$
$$= \mathbf{1}. \tag{4.4}$$

In order that deformations exist corresponding to this representation it is necessary and sufficient that (3.3) be satisfied. Substitution of (4.2) into (3.3) places differential restrictions on **Q** which together with the orthogonality property (4.4) is supposed to be solved in order to determine the set of compatible strains **C**. To find the corresponding deformations, integration of (2.4) must be executed.

Consider the case of two equal principal strains[†]:

$$\lambda \overset{\text{def}}{=} \lambda_1 = \lambda_2, \qquad \mu \overset{\text{def}}{=} \lambda_3. \tag{4.5}$$

In this case (4.2) is readily reduced to

$$C_{ij} = \lambda\delta_{ij} + (\mu - \lambda)u_i u_j, \tag{4.6}$$

with inverse given by

$$C_{ij}^{-1} = [\mu\delta_{ij} - (\mu - \lambda)u_i u_j]/\lambda\mu, \tag{4.7}$$

where $\mathbf{u(X)}$ is an arbitrary unit vector

$$\mathbf{u} \cdot \mathbf{u} = 1. \tag{4.8}$$

Suppose that **u** is represented as the gradient of a potential,[‡]

$$u_i = \varphi_{,i}. \tag{4.9}$$

[†] If all three principal strains are assumed equal, then **C** is constant and Michal's theorem shows that the associated deformation must be homogeneous.

[‡] It is this assumption which introduces loss of completeness in the results.

Then (4.8) becomes

$$\varphi_{,i}\varphi_{,i} = 1, \qquad (4.10)$$

and with the aid of (4.6), (4.7), (2.8), (2.9), and (4.10), the compatibility equations (3.3) become

$$\varphi_{,kr}\varphi_{,pp} - \varphi_{,pk}\varphi_{,pr} = 0. \qquad (4.11)$$

Equations (4.10) and (4.11) pose a nonlinear problem in potential theory which will now be solved to find the (solution) surfaces $\varphi =$ constant.

For later reference it is convenient to replace this system of equations by the equivalent system consisting of (4.10) and

$$\varphi_{,ij} = \sigma v_i v_j, \qquad (4.12)$$

$$\mathbf{v} \cdot \mathbf{v} = 1, \qquad (4.13)$$

$$v_i \varphi_{,i} = 0, \qquad (4.14)$$

where $\sigma(\mathbf{X})$ is an arbitrary (not identically vanishing) scalar function, and where $\mathbf{v}(\mathbf{X})$ denotes an arbitrary unit vector function which by (4.14) is orthogonal to the gradient of φ. To see that this replacement is indeed possible, let $\boldsymbol{\Phi}$ denote the symmetric tensor with components defined by

$$\boldsymbol{\Phi}_{ij} \overset{\text{def}}{=} \varphi_{,ij}.$$

Then (4.11) takes the form

$$\boldsymbol{\Phi} \operatorname{tr} \boldsymbol{\Phi} - \boldsymbol{\Phi}^2 = 0. \qquad (4.15)$$

It is clear that $\boldsymbol{\Phi} = 0$ is a solution of (4.15). However, in this case $\mathbf{u}$ defined in (4.9) and, moreover, $\mathbf{C}$ given by (4.6) are constant, which implies that the deformation is homogeneous. Therefore, we shall assume $\boldsymbol{\Phi} \neq 0$. If, in addition, $\boldsymbol{\Phi}$ is nonsingular, then multiplication of (4.15) by $\boldsymbol{\Phi}^{-1}$ and applying the trace operation yields the result $\operatorname{tr} \boldsymbol{\Phi} = 0$. Recalling (4.15), we obtain the contradiction $\boldsymbol{\Phi} = 0$, which leads to the conclusion that $\boldsymbol{\Phi}$ must be singular:

$$\det \boldsymbol{\Phi} = 0.$$

Applying the trace operation directly to (4.15) we readily see that the second principal invariant of $\boldsymbol{\Phi}$ must also vanish. Therefore, $\boldsymbol{\Phi}$ possesses only one nonzero eigenvalue and admits the type of representation which leads to (4.12) and (4.13). Equation (4.14) follows directly from (4.10), (4.12), and (4.13).

The Gaussian curvature of a surface with unit normal **n** is given† by

$$\tfrac{1}{2}[(n_{i,i})^2 - n_{i,j}n_{i,j} - n_{i,j}n_j n_{i,k}n_k].$$

When this is applied to the solution surface $\varphi = $ constant, since $\varphi_{,i}$ represents the components of its own unit normal we obtain for the Gaussian curvature

$$\tfrac{1}{2}[(\varphi_{,ii})^2 - \varphi_{,ij}\varphi_{,ij}].$$

Therefore, from (4.11) it follows that, in particular, the Gaussian curvature of the solution surface must vanish. With the aid of a well-known theorem in differential geometry‡ we conclude that the solution surface $\varphi(\mathbf{X})$ must be developable, and thus consist of a plane, a cylinder, a cone, or a tangent surface.

We now choose the underlying coordinate system such that the possible solution surfaces may be written in the form

$$\varphi = f(X_\alpha) - AX_3, \tag{4.16}$$

where f denotes a function depending on X_α ($\alpha = 1, 2$), and where A is an arbitrary (possibly zero) constant. Substitution of (4.16) into (4.10), (4.12), and (4.14) yields the following system of equations which in addition to (4.13) are to be solved for $\mathbf{v}$, f, and σ:

$$f_{,\alpha\beta} = \sigma v_\alpha v_\beta, \qquad A^2 + f_{,\alpha}f_{,\alpha} = 1,$$
$$0 = \sigma v_i v_3, \qquad v_3 A + v_\alpha f_{,\alpha} = 0. \tag{4.17}$$

It is clear from the third of (4.17) that A is restricted to the range $|A| \leqslant 1$. Further, for $|A| = 1$ it can be shown that the deformation must be homogeneous since f, for this case is at most constant. Hence, the condition $|A| < 1$ will be adopted.

Since σ and $\mathbf{v}$ do not identically vanish, the second of (4.17) demands that v_3 must be zero. Therefore, (4.13) and the last of (4.17) become, respectively,

$$v_\alpha v_\alpha = 1, \tag{4.18}$$

and

$$v_\alpha f_{,\alpha} = 0. \tag{4.19}$$

Then (4.18) yields, from the first of (4.17), a representation of σ in terms of f which in turn replaces the first of (4.17) by

$$f_{,\alpha\beta} = f_{,\mu\mu}v_\alpha v_\beta. \tag{4.20}$$

---

† See, e.g., Ericksen,[3] Eq. (3.6).
‡ See, e.g., Willmore,[6] p. 107, or Eisenhart,[7] p. 150.

Conversely, for any function f for which $\mathbf{v}$ exists, (4.20) implies (4.18). Further, by multiplication of (4.20) through by $f_{,\beta}$ and use of the third of (4.17) it readily follows that (4.19) is implied. Hence, the remaining problem consists in integrating (4.20) and the third of (4.17) subject to the condition that a nontrivial $\mathbf{v}$ must exist. In order that the latter condition is satisfied it follows from (4.20) that

$$\det(f_{,\alpha\beta} - f_{,\mu\mu}\delta_{\alpha\beta}) = 0,$$

which is equivalent to

$$(f_{,\alpha\alpha})^2 - f_{,\alpha\beta}f_{,\alpha\beta} = 0. \tag{4.21}$$

It is convenient to introduce the function $F(X_\alpha)$ through the definition

$$F \stackrel{\text{def}}{=} f/\sqrt{1 - A^2},$$

which is possible since $A \neq 1$. Then in terms of F, the third of (4.17) and (4.21) become, respectively,

$$F_{,\alpha}F_{,\alpha} = 1, \qquad (F_{,\alpha\alpha})^2 - F_{,\alpha\beta}F_{,\alpha\beta} = 0. \tag{4.22}$$

Applying the two dimensional Laplacian operator to the first of (4.22) and using the second of (4.22) we reach

$$(F_{,\alpha\alpha})^2 + F_{,\alpha\alpha\beta}F_{,\beta} = 0,$$

which may be rewritten as

$$(F_{,\beta}/F_{,\alpha\alpha})_{,\beta} = 2. \tag{4.23}$$

The general solution of (4.23) is

$$F_{,\beta}/F_{,\alpha\alpha} = X_\beta + h_\beta, \tag{4.24}$$

where h_β meets

$$h_{\beta,\beta} = 0. \tag{4.25}$$

Squaring (4.24) and with application of the first of (4.22) we arrive at one expression

$$F_{,\alpha\alpha} = 1/\sqrt{(X_\alpha + h_\alpha)(X_\alpha + h_\alpha)} \tag{4.26}$$

for the quantity $F_{,\alpha\alpha}$ which when substituted into (4.24) yields another formula

$$F_{,\alpha} = (X_\alpha + h_\alpha)/\sqrt{(X_\beta + h_\beta)(X_\beta + h_\beta)}, \tag{4.27}$$

with which $F_{,\alpha\alpha}$ can be calculated. These two equations will be in agreement if and only if h_β meets

$$h_{\alpha,\beta}(X_\alpha + h_\alpha)(X_\beta + h_\beta) = 0. \qquad (4.28)$$

We shall now show that h_α can be at most constant. To this end define the functions k_α and $K_{\alpha\beta}$ through

$$k_\alpha \overset{\text{def}}{=} X_\alpha + h_\alpha,$$

and

$$K_{\alpha\beta} \overset{\text{def}}{=} \tfrac{1}{2}(k_{\alpha,\beta} + k_{\beta,\alpha}).$$

Then (4.25) and (4.28) take the respective forms

$$K_{\alpha\alpha} = 2, \qquad (4.29)$$

and

$$K_{\alpha\beta}k_\alpha k_\beta = k_\alpha k_\alpha, \qquad (4.30)$$

the latter of which can also be written as

$$(\log \sqrt{k_\alpha k_\alpha})_{,\beta}k_\beta = 1. \qquad (4.31)$$

Transforming to the principal axes of $K_{\alpha\beta}$ at an arbitrary selected point $P(X_\alpha)$, (4.29) and (4.30) become

$$K_1 + K_2 = 2, \qquad K_1 k_1{}^2 + K_2 k_2{}^2 = k_1{}^2 + k_2{}^2,$$

where K_α denotes the principal values of $K_{\alpha\beta}$ at P. It follows that provided $k_1 \neq k_2$ at P, then $K_1 = K_2 = 1$, which implies that $K_{\alpha\beta} = \delta_{\alpha\beta}$ at P. If we assume that $k_1 = k_2 \neq 0$ at P, the two equations above reduce to one, and definite conclusions cannot be drawn with this result alone. However, a closer look at (4.31) for this case reveals the contradiction that $K_1 + K_2 = 1$ which leads to the result that the assumption $k_1 = k_2 \neq 0$ is not possible. Finally, we remark that the possibility $k_1 = k_2 = 0$ at P is inadmissible since in this case the first of (4.22) cannot be properly satisfied. Thus, we conclude that $K_{\alpha\beta} = \delta_{\alpha\beta}$ at P, and since P is arbitrary this result must hold at all points. Moreover, this result restricts h_α to be such that

$$h_{\alpha,\beta} + h_{\beta,\alpha} = 0,$$

which can be readily solved to obtain

$$h_\alpha = ce_{\alpha\beta}X_\beta + c_\alpha, \qquad (4.32)$$

where c and c_α are arbitrary constants, and where $e_{\alpha\beta}$ denotes the components of the usual two-dimensional alternator tensor. If we now substitute (4.32) into (4.26) and (4.27) and then use the second of (4.22) it readily follows that c must vanish. Hence h_α is at most constant,

$$h_\alpha = c_\alpha. \tag{4.33}$$

With the aid of (4.33), (4.27) can be integrated to obtain

$$F = \sqrt{(X_\alpha + c_\alpha)(X_\alpha + c_\alpha)}$$

aside from an unessential additive constant, and by a coordinate translation, for convenience, we reach

$$F = \sqrt{X_\alpha X_\alpha}.$$

Hence, with the previous definition of F, (4.16) becomes

$$\varphi = \sqrt{(1 - A^2)X_\alpha X_\alpha} - AX_3, \tag{4.34}$$

which shows that the only possible solution surfaces which meet (4.10) and (4.11) are planes, circular cylinders, and right circular cones.

To calculate the strain and deformation fields associated with (4.34)–(4.9), (4.6), and (2.4), it is convenient to introduce the cylindrical coordinate system (R, Θ, Z) related to X_k through

$$X_1 = R \cos \Theta, \qquad X_2 = R \sin \Theta, \qquad X_3 = Z, \tag{4.35}$$

with (diagonal) metric tensor components $\|G_{kl}\| = (1, R^2, 1)$. Using (4.34), (4.9), and (4.6) and usual tensor transformation laws the covariant components of the strain tensor $\mathbf{C}$ relative to the system (R, Θ, Z) become

$$\|C_{kl}\| = \begin{Vmatrix} \lambda + (\mu - \lambda)(1 - A^2) & 0 & -(\mu - \lambda)A\sqrt{1 - A^2} \\ 0 & \lambda R^2 & 0 \\ -(\mu - \lambda)A\sqrt{1 - A^2} & 0 & \lambda + (\mu - \lambda)A^2 \end{Vmatrix}. \tag{4.36}$$

If, in addition, we introduce the spacial cylindrical coordinate system (r, θ, z) related to x_k through

$$x_1 = r \cos \theta, \qquad x_2 = r \sin \theta, \qquad x_3 = z, \tag{4.37}$$

which possesses a (diagonal) metric tensor with components $\|g_{kl}\| = (1, r^2, 1)$, then the strain-deformation equations (2.4) can be rewritten in terms of (R, Θ, Z) and (r, θ, z) and with the aid of (4.36) are integrable in the form†

$$r = vR, \qquad \theta = \beta\Theta, \qquad z = \gamma R + \eta Z, \qquad (4.38)$$

where the constants v, β, γ, η are not all independent and are related to the constants λ, μ, A. Moreover, in order that the condition of incompressibility (det C = 1) be satisfied it follows that

$$v^4\beta^2\eta^2 = 1. \qquad (4.39)$$

Although the constant strain invariant deformation (4.38) was obtained under the assumption that two of the principal strains are equal it nevertheless remains a deformation of the constant strain invariant class even in general when the four parameters v, β, γ, η are arbitrary. Of course, if incompressibility is to be met then three of the constants are still related through (4.39). Further, we remark that the deformation (4.38) is not generally homogeneous and, therefore, demonstrates that deformations with constant strain invariants need not be of the homogeneous type. In the following section we shall investigate the conditions of equilibrium with regard to (4.38).

5. Equilibrium: Elastic, Incompressible, Isotropic Material

In 1955 Ericksen[8] clearly demonstrated that the only exact solutions possible in (compressible) finite elasticity theory for isotropic homogeneous bodies which are in equilibrium in the absence of body forces are homogeneous deformations. As mentioned previously, this result was conjectured for the case of incompressible materials and in this section we shall investigate the conjecture with respect to deformations (4.38).

The constitutive equation for an elastic, incompressible, isotropic material is

$$\mathbf{T} = -p\mathbf{1} + 2\frac{\partial\Sigma}{\partial\mathrm{I}}\mathbf{B} - 2\frac{\partial\Sigma}{\partial\mathrm{II}}\mathbf{B}^{-1}, \qquad (5.1)$$

where $\mathbf{T}$ denotes the Cauchy stress tensor, p is an arbitrary hydrostatic pressure, $\mathbf{1}$ denotes the unit matrix, $\Sigma = \Sigma(\mathrm{I}, \mathrm{II})$ denotes the strain energy function per unit volume of the undeformed body, and where $\mathbf{B}$

---

† In terms of material and spacial conical coordinates it becomes clear that (4.38) includes the deformation of a circular cone into another circular cone of different apex angle.

represents the left Cauchy–Green tensor defined in terms of the deformation gradient $\mathbf{F}$ by

$$\mathbf{B} \stackrel{\text{def}}{=} \mathbf{F}\mathbf{F}^T. \tag{5.2}$$

In the absence of body forces the equations of equilibrium are

$$\text{div } \mathbf{T} = 0, \tag{5.3}$$

where "div" denotes the spacial tensor divergence operator.

Using (4.38) and (5.2) it is not difficult to show that the mixed components of the tensor $\mathbf{B}$ referred to the cylindrical coordinates $x^k = (r, \theta, z)$ are

$$\|B^k{}_l\| = \begin{Vmatrix} v^2 & 0 & v\gamma \\ 0 & v^2\beta^2 & 0 \\ v\gamma & 0 & \gamma^2 + \eta^2 \end{Vmatrix}. \tag{5.4}$$

With the aid of (5.1) the mixed components of the stress tensor $\mathbf{T}$ with reference to this coordinate system are

$$T^1{}_1 = -p + 2v^2 \frac{\partial \Sigma}{\partial \mathrm{I}} - 2v^2\beta^2(\gamma^2 + \eta^2)\frac{\partial \Sigma}{\partial \mathrm{II}},$$

$$T^2{}_2 = -p + 2v^2\beta^2 \frac{\partial \Sigma}{\partial \mathrm{I}} - 2v^2\eta^2 \frac{\partial \Sigma}{\partial \mathrm{II}},$$

$$T^3{}_3 = -p + 2(\gamma^2 + \eta^2)\frac{\partial \Sigma}{\partial \mathrm{I}} - 2v^4\beta^2 \frac{\partial \Sigma}{\partial \mathrm{II}}, \tag{5.5}$$

$$T^1{}_3 = 2v\gamma\left(\frac{\partial \Sigma}{\partial \mathrm{I}} + v^2\beta^2 \frac{\partial \Sigma}{\partial \mathrm{II}}\right),$$

$$T^1{}_2 = T^2{}_3 = 0,$$

and substitution into the equilibrium equations (5.3) results in the integrability conditions

$$v\gamma\left(\frac{\partial \Sigma}{\partial \mathrm{I}} + v^2\beta^2 \frac{\partial \Sigma}{\partial \mathrm{II}}\right) = 0, \tag{5.6}$$

which is both necessary and sufficient for the existence of p. In order that incompressibility (4.39) be satisfied it is clear that $v \neq 0$. Hence,

(5.6) will be met if either $\gamma = 0$, or if the parameters v, β, γ, and η are such that $(\partial\Sigma/\partial I) + v^2\beta^2 \, \partial\Sigma/\partial II = 0$. In the former case the deformation (4.38) reduces to

$$r = vR, \qquad \theta = \beta\Theta, \qquad z = \eta Z, \qquad (5.7)$$

where the parameters v, β, η are subject to the incompressibility condition (4.39). The deformation (5.7) possesses constant strain invariants, is not homogeneous, and satisfies equilibrium for incompressible elastic bodies irregardless of the particular strain energy function. Therefore, it represents a counterexample to Ericksen's conjecture. However, it is not a new exact solution and serves only to raise the question of whether there exists new exact solutions of the constant strain invariant type. (See footnote ($\ddagger$) on page 109.)

In the latter case the condition $(\partial\Sigma/\partial I) + v^2\beta^2 \, \partial\Sigma/\partial II = 0$ represents a restriction on the strain energy function which, at best, can be satisfied for only particular elastic materials. Moreover, certain experimental[9] and theoretical[10] results indicate that this condition may not even be possible for any elastic materials.

REFERENCES

1. C. Truesdell and R. Toupin, The classical field theories, *in* "Handbuch der Physik" (S. Flügge, ed.), Vol. 3, pp. 226–793. Springer, Berlin, 1960.
2. K. Washizu, A note on the conditions of compatibility, *J. Math. and Phys.* **36**, 306–312 (1958).
3. J. L. Ericksen, Deformations possible in every isotropic, incompressible, perfectly elastic body, *Z. Angew. Math. Phys.* **5**, 466–489 (1954).
4. M. Singh and A. C. Pipkin, Note on Ericksen's problem, *Z. Angew. Math. Phys.* **16**, 706–709 (1965).
5. A. D. Michal, "Matrix and Tensor Calculus." Wiley, New York, 1947.
6. T. J. Willmore, "An Introduction to Differential Geometry." Oxford Univ. Press (Clarendon), London and New York, 1959.
7. L. P. Eisenhart, "An Introduction to Differential Geometry." Princeton Univ. Press, Princeton, New Jersey, 1947.
8. J. L. Ericksen, Deformations possible in every isotropic, compressible, perfectly elastic material, *J. Math. and Phys.* **34**, 126–128 (1955).
9. R. S. Rivlin and D. W. Saunders, Large elastic deformations of isotropic materials VII. Experiments on the deformation of rubber, *Phil. Trans. Roy. Soc. (London)* **A243**, 251–288 (1951).
10. C. Truesdell and R. Toupin, Static grounds for inequalities in finite strain of elastic materials, *Arch. Rational Mech. Anal.* **12**, 1–33 (1963).

A Representative Theorem for the Constitutive Equation of Simple Material in Motions with Constant Stretch History

C.-C. WANG

Department of Mechanics
The Johns Hopkins University
Baltimore, Maryland

According to Coleman (1962) a *substantially stagnant motion* or a *motion with constant stretch history* is one for which at each instant t there exists an orthonormal basis $\{e_i(t)\}$ such that the components relative to the basis of the relative Cauchy–Green tensor $C_{(t)}(t - s)$ depend only on the time lapse s, or equivalently, if there exists an orthogonal tensor function $Q(t)$ such that

$$C_{(t)}(t - s) = Q(t)C_{(0)}(0 - s)Q(t)^T, \qquad t, s \in (-\infty, \infty)$$

Later, Noll (1962) gave a representation for the class of motions with constant stretch history: *A motion has constant stretch history if and only if the relative deformation gradient* $F_{(0)}(\tau)$ *is of the form*

$$F_{(0)}(\tau) = Q(\tau)\exp(\tau A), \qquad \tau \in (-\infty, \infty)$$

where A *is a constant tensor and where* $Q(\tau)$ *is an orthogonal tensor function such that*

$$Q(0) = 1.$$

Noll then classified the motions with constant stretch history into the following three categories:
  (i)   Viscometric flows, $A^2 = 0$.
  (ii) Flows in which $A^2 \neq 0$ but $A^3 = 0$.
  (iii) Flows in which $A^n \neq 0$, $\forall n$.
Using the representation theorem Noll also obtained criterions for these three categories of flows.

We remark here that the viscometric flows include many interesting steady flows such as simple shearing flow, Couette flow, Poiseuille flow, helical flow, etc., for which the dynamical equations can be solved for incompressible simple fluids. These solutions were first obtained by

Rivlin (1956) for incompressible Rivlin–Ericksen fluids and later by Coleman and Noll (1959a) for incompressible simple fluids. Coleman and Noll (1959b) also obtained solutions for a class of flows called *steady extensions* which are special cases of the third category of motions with constant stretch history. The steady extension can be characterized by the condition

$$\mathbf{A}_n = \mathbf{A}_1{}^n, \qquad \forall n,$$

where $\mathbf{A}_k$, $k = 1, 2, \ldots$ denotes the kth Rivlin–Ericksen tensor of the motion. For incompressible simple fluids only isochoric steady extensions are possible. Thus,

$$\mathrm{tr}\,\mathbf{A}_1 = 0.$$

The main theorem which I shall prove here is the following:

THEOREM. *In a motion with constant history the relative Cauchy–Green tensor $\mathbf{C}_{(t)}(t - s)$, regarded as a function of s, is uniquely determined by the first three Rivlin–Ericksen tensors $\mathbf{A}_1(t)$, $\mathbf{A}_2(t)$, $\mathbf{A}_3(t)$ at the fixed instant t.*

Consequently, within the class of motions with constant stretch history the stress in a simple material depends only on the first three Rivlin–Ericksen tensors and the deformation gradient from some fixed reference configuration. More specifically, the constitutive equation of a simple material reduces to the form

$$\mathbf{T}^*(t) = \mathbf{G}(\mathbf{A}_1{}^*(t), \mathbf{A}_2{}^*(t), \mathbf{A}_3{}^*(t), \mathbf{C}(t))$$

where $\mathbf{C}(t)$ is the Cauchy–Green tensor relative to the fixed reference configuration and where

$$\mathbf{T}^*(t) = \mathbf{R}(t)^T \mathbf{T}(t)\mathbf{R}(t), \qquad \mathbf{A}_k{}^*(t) = \mathbf{R}(t)^T \mathbf{A}_k(t)\mathbf{R}(t), \qquad \forall k,$$

are the rotated stress tensor and the rotated Rivlin–Ericksen tensors, respectively. Here, $\mathbf{R}(t)$ denotes the finite rotation from the fixed reference configuration. In particular, if the simple material is a simple fluid, then the constitutive equation reduces to that of a special Rivlin–Ericksen fluid, i.e.,

$$\mathbf{T}(t) = \mathbf{G}(\mathbf{A}_1(t), \mathbf{A}_2(t), \mathbf{A}_3(t), \rho(t))$$

where $\rho(t)$ is the mass density. In this sense, the solutions obtained by Coleman and Noll (1959a) for simple fluids in viscometric flows are no more general than the earlier solutions obtained by Rivlin (1956), since from the reduced form of the constitutive equation the behavior of a simple fluid in the class of motions with constant stretch history cannot be distinguished from that of a special Rivlin–Ericksen fluid.

The first three Rivlin–Ericksen tensors of a motion with constant stretch history are not entirely arbitrary. They must satisfy certain compatibility conditions which I shall *not* present in this paper. I simply mention some special cases. It turns out that the viscometric flows and the steady extensions are completely determined by $\mathbf{A}_1(t)$ and $\mathbf{A}_2(t)$. In fact, a motion with constant stretch history is a steady extension if and only if

$$\mathbf{A}_2 = \mathbf{A}_1{}^2,$$

while a motion with constant stretch history is a viscometric flow if and only if relative to the principal orthonormal basis of $\mathbf{A}_1$ the component matrices of $\mathbf{A}_1$ and $\mathbf{A}_2$ are of the form

$$[\mathbf{A}_1] = \begin{bmatrix} k & 0 & 0 \\ 0 & -k & 0 \\ 0 & 0 & 0 \end{bmatrix}, \quad [\mathbf{A}_2] = \begin{bmatrix} k^2 & -k^2 & 0 \\ -k^2 & k^2 & 0 \\ 0 & 0 & 0 \end{bmatrix}.$$

Of course, in any case a motion with constant stretch history is completely determined by the first three Rivlin–Ericksen tensors. Hence, we do not have to calculate $\mathbf{A}_4$, $\mathbf{A}_5$, and $\mathbf{A}_6$ as in the criterion obtained by Noll (1962) for the various categories of motions with constant stretch history.

Before we prove the main theorem I, first state a simple lemma:

LEMMA. *Let* $[\mathbf{S}]$ *be a* 3×3 *diagonal matrix and let* $[\mathbf{W}]$ *be a* 3×3 *skew symmetric matrix:*

$$[\mathbf{S}] = \begin{bmatrix} a & 0 & 0 \\ 0 & b & 0 \\ 0 & 0 & c \end{bmatrix}, \quad [\mathbf{W}] = \begin{bmatrix} 0 & x & y \\ -x & 0 & z \\ -y & -z & 0 \end{bmatrix}.$$

Then the following are three pairs of equivalent statements:

(i)a, $a \neq b \neq c$,
   b, $[\mathbf{SW}] = [\mathbf{WS}]$ if and only if $[\mathbf{W}] = [\mathbf{0}]$.
(ii)a, $a = b \neq c$,
   b, $[\mathbf{SW}] = [\mathbf{WS}]$ if and only if $y = z = 0$.
(iii)a, $a = b = c$,
   b, $[\mathbf{SW}] = [\mathbf{WS}], \forall[\mathbf{W}]$.

In application we shall interpret [S] and [W] to be the component matrices of a symmetric and a skew symmetric tensor relative to the principal orthonormal basis of **S**. Then the lemma gives necessary and sufficient conditions for the commutativity of **S** and **W**.

We now prove the main theorem.

Proof. From Noll's representation theorem it is easily verified that the relative Cauchy–Green tensor in a motion with constant stretch history is given by

$$\mathbf{C}_{(t)}(t - s) = \exp(-s\mathbf{L}^T)\exp(-s\mathbf{L})$$

where

$$\mathbf{L} \equiv \mathbf{L}(t) \equiv \mathbf{Q}(t)\mathbf{A}\mathbf{Q}(t)^T.$$

We compute the Rivlin–Ericksen tensors by the formula

$$\mathbf{A}_k(t) = (-1)^k \frac{d^k}{ds^k}\mathbf{C}_{(t)}(t - s)\Big|_{s=0}.$$

It is easily shown that the following recurrence relation holds in motions with constant stretch history:

$$\mathbf{A}_1 \equiv \mathbf{A}_1(t) = \mathbf{L}^T + \mathbf{L},$$
$$\mathbf{A}_2 \equiv \mathbf{A}_2(t) = \mathbf{L}^T\mathbf{A}_1 + \mathbf{A}_1\mathbf{L},$$

.

.

.

$$\mathbf{A}_k \equiv \mathbf{A}_k(t) = \mathbf{L}^T\mathbf{A}_{k-1} + \mathbf{A}_{k-1}\mathbf{L}, \qquad k = 2, 3, \cdots.$$

We consider the following three cases:
(i) $\mathbf{A}_1$ has three distinct proper numbers. We claim that in this case the tensor **L** is uniquely determined by $\mathbf{A}_1$ and $\mathbf{A}_2$.
(ii) $\mathbf{A}_1$ has only two distinct proper numbers. Thus relative to the principal orthonormal basis the component matrix of $\mathbf{A}_1$ has the form

$$[\mathbf{A}_1] = \begin{bmatrix} a & 0 & 0 \\ 0 & a & 0 \\ 0 & 0 & b \end{bmatrix}, \qquad a \neq b.$$

We consider the following two subcases:

(iia) Relative to the principal orthonormal basis of $\mathbf{A}_1$ the component matrix of $\mathbf{A}_2$ is of the form

$$[\mathbf{A}_2] = \begin{bmatrix} u & 0 & 0 \\ 0 & u & 0 \\ 0 & 0 & v \end{bmatrix}, \qquad \text{where} \quad u \neq v.$$

In this subcase we claim that we must have

$$u = a^2, \qquad v = b^2,$$

and that the relative Cauchy-Green tensor $\mathbf{C}_{(t)}(t - s)$, regarded as a function of s, is uniquely determined by $\mathbf{A}_1$ and $\mathbf{A}_2$. The tensor $\mathbf{L}$, however, is *not* uniquely determined. In fact, the component matrix of $\mathbf{L}$ relative to the orthonormal basis of $\mathbf{A}_1$ is of the form

$$[\mathbf{L}] = \begin{bmatrix} a/2 & x & 0 \\ -x & a/2 & 0 \\ 0 & 0 & b/2 \end{bmatrix}$$

where x is arbitrary. But the class of all such $\mathbf{L}$'s determines only one $\mathbf{C}_{(t)}(t - s)$, namely

$$\mathbf{C}_{(t)}(t - s) = \exp(-s\mathbf{A}_1).$$

(iib) Relative to the principal orthonormal basis of $\mathbf{A}_1$ the component matrix of $\mathbf{A}_2$ is *not* of the form in (iia). We claim that in this subcase the tensor $\mathbf{L}$ is uniquely determined by $\mathbf{A}_1$, $\mathbf{A}_2$, and $\mathbf{A}_3$.

(iii) $\mathbf{A}_1$ has only one proper number, i.e., $\mathbf{A}_1 = a\mathbf{1}$. We claim that in this case the relative Cauchy–Green tensor $\mathbf{C}_{(t)}(t - s)$ is of the form

$$\mathbf{C}_{(t)}(t - s) = \exp(-as\mathbf{1}).$$

Again, $\mathbf{L}$ is *not* unique. In fact,

$$\mathbf{L} = \tfrac{1}{2}a\mathbf{1} + \mathbf{W}$$

where $\mathbf{W}$ is an arbitrary skew symmetric tensor.

I shall prove only the claim made in case (i). The other two cases can be proved in similar way.

Recall that the Rivlin–Ericksen tensors in a motion with constant stretch history satisfy the recurrence relation

$$\mathbf{A}_1 = \mathbf{L}^T + \mathbf{L}, \qquad \mathbf{A}_2 = \mathbf{L}^T\mathbf{A}_1 + \mathbf{A}_1\mathbf{L}.$$

In case (i) we have assumed that $\mathbf{A}_1$ has three *distinct* proper numbers. By the lemma we see that $\mathbf{A}_1$ does not commute with any nonzero skew symmetric tensor. Now suppose that our claim were not correct. Then we can find another tensor $\overline{\mathbf{L}}$ such that

$$\overline{\mathbf{L}}^T + \overline{\mathbf{L}} = \mathbf{L}^T + \mathbf{L}, \qquad \overline{\mathbf{L}}^T\mathbf{A}_1 + \mathbf{A}_1\overline{\mathbf{L}} = \mathbf{L}^T\mathbf{A}_1 + \mathbf{A}_1\mathbf{L}.$$

Thus, the difference $\overline{\mathbf{L}} - \mathbf{L}$ is skew, and it commutes with $\mathbf{A}_1$. Hence, $\mathbf{L} = \overline{\mathbf{L}}$.

Since, obviously, the three cases exhaust all possibilities, our main theorem is proved. Notice that only in subcase (iib) do we need $\mathbf{A}_1$, $\mathbf{A}_2$, $\mathbf{A}_3$ to determine $\mathbf{C}_{(t)}(t - s)$. Fortunately, the viscometric flows and the steady extension do not belong to this subcase. Thus, criterions for these two classes of flows involve only $\mathbf{A}_1$ and $\mathbf{A}_2$, as I indicated before. We remark here again that $\mathbf{A}_1$, $\mathbf{A}_2$, and $\mathbf{A}_3$ are not independent. The compatibility conditions are given in Wang (1966). These compatibility conditions, however, do serve an important purpose: they enable us to determine whether a given motion is a motion with constant stretch history.

We insert here a brief discussion on the position of motions with constant stretch history in the general linear group $GL(3, R)$. In Noll's theory of simple material a *local experiment* is represented by a regular tensor function $\mathbf{F}(t - s)$, $s \in [0, \infty)$ called the *deformation history* up to the instant t. The value of the deformation history $\mathbf{F}(t - s)$ is the *deformation gradient* at time $t - s$ relative to some fixed local reference configuration. The stress tensor $\mathbf{T}(t)$ at the instant t in a simple material is a function of the deformation history, i.e., a simple material is defined by the constitutive equation

$$\mathbf{T}(t) = \overset{\infty}{\underset{s=0}{\mathscr{F}}} (\mathbf{F}(t - s)).$$

From the principle of material frame-indifference, the functional $\mathscr{F}$ satisfies the identity

$$\overset{\infty}{\underset{s=0}{\mathscr{F}}} (\mathbf{Q}(s)\mathbf{F}(t - s)) = \mathbf{Q}(0) \overset{\infty}{\underset{s=0}{\mathscr{F}}} (\mathbf{F}(t - s))\mathbf{Q}(0)^T$$

for all orthogonal tensor functions $Q(s)$, $s \in [0, \infty)$. Thus if $\mathbf{F}(t - s)$, $\overline{\mathbf{F}}(t - s)$, $s \in [0, \infty)$ are two deformation histories such that

$$\overline{\mathbf{F}}(t - s) = \mathbf{Q}(s)\mathbf{F}(t - s), \qquad s \in [0, \infty)$$

for some orthogonal tensor function $\mathbf{Q}(s)$, then the stress tensor $\mathbf{T}(t)$ and $\overline{\mathbf{T}}(t)$ corresponding to $\mathbf{F}(t - s)$ and $\overline{\mathbf{F}}(t - s)$, respectively, are related by the formula

$$\overline{\mathbf{T}}(t) = \mathbf{Q}(0)\mathbf{T}(t)\mathbf{Q}(0)^T.$$

We shall call these two deformation histories $\mathbf{F}(t - s)$ and $\overline{\mathbf{F}}(t - s)$ *equivalent*. Obviously, two histories are equivalent if and only if they have the same Cauchy–Green tensor $\mathbf{C}(t - s)$, $s \in [0, \infty)$.

Suppose $\mathbf{F}(t - s)$ is a deformation history. We define the *relative deformation history* $\mathbf{F}_{(t)}(t - s)$ by

$$\mathbf{F}_{(t)}(t - s) \equiv \mathbf{F}(t - s)\mathbf{F}(t)^{-1}.$$

It is easily seen that the value of the relative deformation history is an intrinsic property of the deformation history, since $\mathbf{F}_{(t)}(t - s)$ is *independent* of the reference configuration. From the constitutive equation we see that the stress tensor $\mathbf{T}(t)$ is a function of the relative deformation history and the deformation gradient at the instant t.

From a pure mathematical point of view, a deformation history $\mathbf{F}(t - s)$, $s \in [0, \infty)$ is just a parametered curve in the general linear group $GL(3, R)$. The time lapse s is the parameter of the curve. The general linear group $GL(3, R)$ is a Lie group. Its Lie algebra is the algebra of all right invariant vector fields relative to the bracket product. The integral curves of these right invariant vector fields are of the form

$$\mathbf{F}(\tau) = \exp(\tau\mathbf{A})\mathbf{B}, \qquad \tau \in (-\infty, \infty)$$

where $\mathbf{A}$ is the value of the right invariant field at the identity $\mathbf{1}$, τ is the parameter of the integral curve, and $\mathbf{B}$ is the point on the integral curve corresponding to $\tau = 0$. If we set $\tau = t - s$ then the parametered curve $\mathbf{F}(t - s)$, $s \in [0, \infty)$ becomes a deformation history where $\mathbf{B}$ is the deformation gradient at time 0, i.e.,

$$\mathbf{F}(t - s) = \exp((t - s)\mathbf{A})\mathbf{F}(0), \qquad s \in [0, \infty).$$

A deformation history of this form is called an *invariant motion*.

In an invariant motion it is easily shown that the relative deformation history is given by

$$\mathbf{F}_{(t)}(t - s) = \exp(-s\mathbf{A}).$$

Thus, $\mathbf{F}_{(t)}(t - s)$ is independent of t. Conversely, suppose that for a given motion the relative deformation history $F_{(t)}(t - s)$ is independent of t, i.e.,

$$F_{(t)}(t - s) = G(s), \qquad s \in (-\infty, \infty) \tag{*}$$

where $G(s)$ is a fixed function for all t. Then it is easily shown that $G(s)$ forms an one parametered group, i.e.,

$$G(0) = 1$$

and

$$G(s + r) = G(s)G(r), \qquad \forall r, s.$$

Under a minor continuity assumption these conditions imply that

$$G(s) = \exp(-sA).$$

Thus, (*) is necessary and sufficient for an invariant motion.

A motion which is equivalent to an invariant motion is given by

$$F(t - s) = Q(s) \exp((t - s)A)B$$

where $Q(s)$ is an orthogonal tensor function. Thus, the relative deformation gradient is given by

$$F_{(t)}(t - s) = Q(s)Q(0)^{-1} \exp((t - s)Q(0)AQ(0)^{-1}).$$

Put

$$\bar{Q}(s) = Q(s)Q(0)^{-1}, \qquad \bar{A} = Q(0)AQ(0)^{-1}, \qquad t = 0,$$

we then get

$$F_{(0)}(\tau) = \bar{Q}(\tau) \exp(\tau\bar{A}). \tag{†}$$

Comparing (†) with Noll's representation theorem we see that the motion is a motion with constant stretch history. Since $\bar{Q}(\tau)$ and A are both arbitrary, we can get every motion with constant stretch history this way. Thus, we have the following:

PROPOSITION. *A motion has constant stretch history if and only if it is equivalent to an invariant motion.*

We now go back to the necessary and sufficient condition (*) for an invariant motion. Suppose that we *define* an invariant motion by (*), and we *define* a motion with constant stretch history by the proposition. Then it is easily shown that (*) and this definition of a motion with constant stretch history is equivalent to that of Coleman. In this sense Noll's representation theorem is a consequence of (†).

REFERENCES

Coleman, B. D. (1962). *Trans. Soc. Rheol.* **6**, 293–300.
Coleman, B. D. and Noll, W. (1959a). *Arch. Rational Mech. Anal.* **3**, 289–311.
Coleman, B. D. and Noll, W. (1959b). *J. Appl. Phys.* **30**, 1508–1512.
Noll, W. (1962). *Arch. Rational Mech. Anal.* **11**, 97–105.
Rivlin, R. S. (1956). *J. Rational Mech. Anal.* **5**, 179–188.
Wang, C.-C. (1966). *Arch. Rational Mech. Anal.* **20**, 329–340.

The Problem of a Jet against the Ground Rheological Solution in the Hodograph Plane

R. GOETHALS and TH. ALZIARY DE ROQUEFORT

E.N.S.M.A.

University of Poitiers
Poitiers, France

The study of the performances of ground effect machines (or air cushion vehicles) requires the solution of the problem of jet emitted in the direction of a wall.

1. We consider here the problem of a two-dimensional jet plane (Fig. 1) in which the solid boundaries OA, $O'A'$, and BC are rectilinear. We assume that the flow is incompressible and irrotational. Then there exists a potential of the velocities (x, y). The problem can be resolved by Kirchhoff's method, as shown by Strand[1] and Ehrich,[2] but the calculations are lengthy.

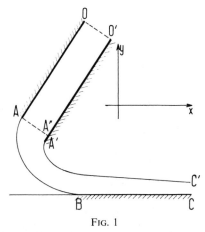

FIG. 1

The difficulty one encounters with the rheoelectric analogy in its classical form is that the limits of AB and $A'C'$ are not known. The boundary conditions are:
  (i) the velocity direction is known on OA, $O'A'$, and BC;
  (ii) the velocity is constant on AB and $A'C'$ (Bernoulli).

Hence, the boundaries in the hodograph plane, which we see in Fig. 2, are known.

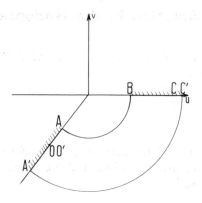

Fig. 2

2. The potential ϕ is a harmonic function of x and y:

$$\frac{\partial^2 \phi}{\partial x^2} + \frac{\partial^2 \phi}{\partial y^2} = 0$$

We can show that it is also a harmonic function of the velocity components u and v. Indeed, ϕ is the real part of the analytic function $F(z)$ (with $z = x + iy$). We know that the derivative $dF/dz = u - iv = w$ is also an analytic function of z. Conversely, z is an analytic function of w, and $F\{z(w)\}$ is also an analytic function of w. Therefore, its real part is a harmonic function of u and v. Thus,

$$\frac{\partial^2 \phi}{\partial u^2} + \frac{\partial^2 \phi}{\partial v^2} = 0$$

Using this equation and the rheoelectric analogy, we can find the potential in the hodograph plane. In the direct analogy, identifying the electrical potential v with the velocity potential ϕ, on $OABC$ and $O'A'C'$ we have $\partial\phi/\partial n = 0$ which is also valid in the hodograph plane. Therefore, the model conductor is the part $AA'C'B$. The flow is then transformed into a source on OO' and a sink on CC' and the flow of electricity is to the corresponding points of the plane Ouv.

In practice, it is not possible to represent the equipotential lines OO' and CC' at infinity: this would require pinpoint electrodes and an infinite potential difference. The boundary conditions on OO' and CC' are therefore fixed at distances that are as large as possible and that depend, above all, on the size of the electrodes.

3. Thus, we obtain the potential in the hodograph plane $\phi(u, v)$. This result is transformed in the physical plane in the following manner.
We have

$$d\phi = u\,dx + v\,dy$$

but on a streamline

$$\frac{dy}{dx} = \frac{v}{u}$$

and

$$d\phi = \frac{u^2 + v^2}{u}\,dx = \frac{u^2 + v^2}{v}\,dy$$

Hence

$$x - x_0 = \int_{\phi_0}^{\phi} \frac{u}{u^2 + v^2}\,d\phi$$

and

$$y - y_0 = \int_{\phi_0}^{\phi} \frac{v}{u^2 + v^2}\,d\phi$$

These integrals must be calculated on a streamline.

4. The problem is resolved in the following way:
We are given the angle between the nozzle walls OA and $O'A'$ and the ground BC and the ratio of the velocities on AB and $A'C'$ which determine the area of the hodograph plane. The input is provided by two electrodes, as narrow as possible, situated on OO' and CC' on the straight lines AA' and BC. The two corresponding equipotentials are therefore perpendicular to OA and BC, respectively. The position of the electrode OO' remains to be determined. For this, we have

$$x_{A'} - x_A = (x_c - x_A) - (x_{c'} - x_{A'})$$

$$x_{A'} - x_A = \int_{ABC} \frac{u}{u^2 + v^2}\,d\phi - \int_{A'C'} \frac{u}{u^2 + v^2}\,d\phi$$

and A'' being the projection of A on $O'A'$,

$$y_{A''} - y_{A'} = (y_A - y_0) - (y_{A'} - y_{0'})$$

$$y_{A''} - y_{A'} = \int_{OA} \frac{v \, d\phi}{u^2 + v^2} - \int_{O'A'} \frac{v \, d\phi}{u^2 + v^2}$$

The position of OO' therefore fixes the ratio $(y_{A''} - y_A)/(x_{A'} - x_A)$, that is to say, the relative position of the nozzle. When the relative position of the nozzle is given, the position of OO' is easily determined by successive approximations.

We can control the dimensions of the electrodes OO' and CC' and make them small enough in calculating the lengths OA and BC for example, which must be large compared to the width AA'' of the jet and the height of A above the ground.

5. In summary, we determine the form of the jet and especially its height above the ground, corresponding to a fixed nozzle configuration and to a fixed velocity ratio.

The same principle of calculation is applied to the case of a forced jet (Figs. 3 and 4). The feeder arrives on the model on OO', BB', and CC'. The ratio of the outputs on each side constitutes additional known quantities. This ratio is easily fixed in measuring the intensity of the currents passing through BB' and CC' which are proportional to the mass flow.

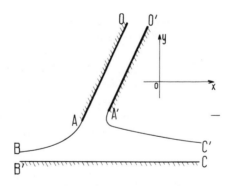

FIG. 3

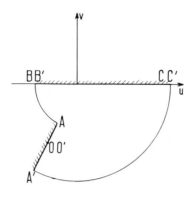

FIG. 4

FIG. 4

6. We can easily find the results of the thin jet theory and of the improvement proposed by Pinnes.[3] It suffices to suppose that AA' and BC are equipotentials in the hodograph plane (Fig. 5). The streamlines are then arcs of a circle and the equipotentials straight segments issuing from the origin. Let θ be the angle of the velocity with the x-axis and V_1 and V_2 the exterior and interior velocities, respectively. We have

$$d\phi = KV\, d\theta \qquad \text{with} \quad KV = C^{st} = K_1V_1 = K_2V_2$$

The transformation formulas give, on a streamline,

$$x - x_0 = K\int_{\theta_0}^{\theta} \cos\theta\, d\theta = K(\sin\theta - \sin\theta_0)$$

$$y - y_0 = K\int_{\theta_0}^{\theta} \sin\theta\, d\theta = K(\cos\theta_0 - \cos\theta)$$

The streamlines in the physical plane are therefore arcs of a circle with radius K and a common center.

Let a be the width of the jet. If $V_2 - V_1$ is small,

$$p_2 - p_1 \begin{cases} = \rho V^2\left(1 - \dfrac{V_2}{V_1}\right) = \rho V^2\left(1 - \dfrac{K_1}{K_2}\right) = \dfrac{\rho V^2 a}{K_2} \\[2mm] = \dfrac{\rho V^2 a}{h}(1 - \cos\theta_0) \end{cases}$$

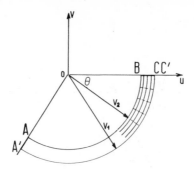

FIG. 5

This is the result of the thin jet theory. If we do not use the hypothesis that $V_2 - V_1$ is small,

$$p_2 - p_1 = \frac{\rho V^2}{2}\left(1 - \frac{V_2^{\ 2}}{V_1^{\ 2}}\right) = \frac{\rho V^2}{2}\left(1 - \frac{K_1^{\ 2}}{K_2^{\ 2}}\right)$$

$$\frac{K_1}{K_2} = 1 - \frac{a(1 - \cos\theta_0)}{h - a\cos\theta_0} = \frac{h - a}{h - a\cos\theta_0}$$

and

$$p_2 - p_1 = \frac{1}{2}\rho V_1^{\ 2}\left\{1 - \left(\frac{1 - \dfrac{a}{h}}{1 - \dfrac{a}{h}\cos\theta_0}\right)^2\right\}$$

Again, we find the improvement proposed by Pinnes.[3]

REFERENCES

1. T. Strand, Inviscid incompressible flow theory of static peripheral jets in proximity to the ground, *J.A.S.* **28**, No. 1.
2. F. Ehrich, The curtain jet, *J.A.S.* **28**, No. 11.
3. R. W. Pinnes, A power plan man's look at the ground effect machine, Bur. of Aeronautics, Navy Dept. Research, Rept. DR-1958 (April, 1959).

Some Interpretations of the Toms Effect†

A. G. FABULA,‡ J. L. LUMLEY,§ and W. D. TAYLOR¶

The Pennsylvania State University
University Park, Pennsylvania

The turbulent-flow friction reduction produced by very low concentrations of linear macromolecules in good solvents has been shown by at least three investigators to occur only when the pipe wall shear stress τ_w exceeds a particular "threshold" value τ_{wt} for each polymer. The concentration dependence of τ_{wt} is not yet clear, but seems to be small. Some other results which show a very different type of concentration dependence can be attributed to poorer mixing, giving a different state of macromolecular aggregation. Available data for τ_{wt} suggest a correlation with parameters of the macromolecular coil, e.g., unperturbed-coil radius of gyration $\langle s^2 \rangle^{1/2}$ and zeroshear intrinsic viscosity $[\eta]$. Virk has hypothesized that the threshold is reached when some smallest significant scale of the turbulence near the wall becomes small enough with respect to coil diameter, taken as $2\langle s^2 \rangle^{1/2}$. However, current turbulence theory suggests that the smallest significant scale is roughly 100 times larger at the threshold.

A feature of the Toms effect and the associated turbulent flow structure is apparently a thickened "viscous sublayer" and for the very effective additives, perhaps also a greatly thickened "buffer zone." Various possible hypotheses to explain the Toms effect and/or the friction reduction threshold are considered. First, a molecular viscoelasticity hypothesis is tested which yields rough agreement with Virk's experimental data but with $\langle s^2 \rangle \tau_{wt}^{3/2} \approx$ constant, instead of $\langle s^2 \rangle \tau_{wt} \approx$ constant suggested by Virk, the latter fitting the experimental data better. However it is thought that noninteracting macromolecules are not likely to

† The work of A. G. Fabula was supported by the U.S. Bureau of Naval Weapons as a part of the graduate study program in Hydrodynamics of Submerged Bodies jointly in the Department of Aeronautical Engineering and the Garfield Thomas Water Tunnel of the Ordnance Research Laboratory. The work of J. L. Lumley was supported by the U.S. Office of Naval Research under Contract Nonr 656(33).

‡ *Present address*: U.S. Naval Ordnance Test Station, Pasadena, California.

§ Department of Aeronautical Engineering.

¶ Department of Biophysics.

produce significant viscoelasticity nor to thicken the buffer zone. The effectiveness of dilute concentrations suggests that local concentrations of macromolecules are occurring. Thus, it is notable that a critical particle Reynolds number found to determine the onset of rigid particle migration in laminar flow leads to the relation $\langle s^2 \rangle \tau_{wt} \approx$ constant. Thus the presence of clusters of macromolecules is hypothesized, which are stretched out into gelatinous fibers in the high-shear regions. It is noted that the maximum volume fraction of such fibers would be approximately $c[\eta]$, and, thus, the friction reduction in dilute polymer solutions with $c[\eta] \approx 0.01$ is comparable with the reduction in fiber suspensions with 1% volume fraction of fibers. Finally, the possibility is discussed that the macromolecules or clusters thereof produce a modification of the intense shear layers associated with longitudinal vortices near the wall in turbulent boundary layers and pipe flows.

1. Introduction

Recent experimental results, especially those of Elata and Tirosh,[1] Virk,[2] and Elata and Lehrer[3] show that the onset of the Toms effect, i.e., the friction reduction in turbulent pipe flow of very dilute solutions of high molecular weight linear polymers, is associated with characteristic threshold wall shear stresses. Virk used poly(ethylene oxide) (PEO) in water in a pipe of 0.292-cm diameter, while Elata, Tirosh, and Lehrer used guar gum in water in pipes of 1- to 5-cm diameter. The behavior can also be seen in the early observations of friction reduction in very dilute polymer solutions by Toms,[4] for polymethyl methacrylate in monochlorobenzene. Figure 1 is a replot of some of Toms' data by Savins,[5] in terms of friction coefficient f vs Reynolds number, Re, for

$$f \equiv \tau_w \bigg/ \frac{\rho}{2}\overline{U}^2 \qquad \mathrm{Re} \equiv \rho \overline{U} D / \eta_1$$

where τ_w is the pipe wall shear stress inferred from the pressure drop per unit length, ρ is the solution density, $\overline{U}$ is the bulk mean speed, D is the pipe inner diameter, and η_1 is a reference viscosity. Toms used a high-shear viscosity of his solutions for η_1, but in recent work the solvent viscosity has often been used in such plots because the very dilute solutions of interest have viscosities which vary little with shear rate and which are close to that of the solvent.[6] For the larger tube used by Toms, the relation of the friction coefficient curves for solution and solvent in the larger tube in Fig. 1 is just as described by the mentioned investigators: below a threshold wall shear stress, τ_{wt}, which is rather insensitive to concentration according to these investigators, the very

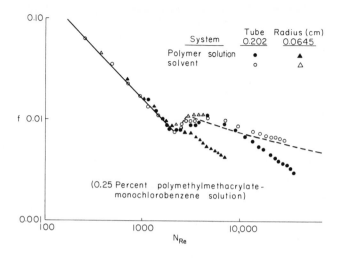

F𝑖𝑔. 1   An illustration of threshold wall shear stress behavior (data from Toms,[4] replotted by Savins[5]).

dilute solution behaves in turbulent flow like a Newtonian fluid, while for a considerable range of $\tau_w > \tau_{wt}$ there is a monotonic increase of flow rate relative to that of the solvent as concentration increases. While the friction coefficient curve for the smaller tube used by Toms does not imply a τ_{wt} value directly, one can infer a value by extrapolating the solvent and solution curves for fully turbulent flow.

The question of concentration dependence of the threshold stress is not fully settled. Theoretical reasoning, such as that given later, suggests that the threshold condition corresponds to a characteristic shear rate, rather than a characteristic shear stress. Thus, the threshold shear stress should increase linearly with solution viscosity, η. Experimentally, Virk has concluded that τ_{wt} is independent of concentration, while Elata and Lehrer find that their threshold stress values can allow either $\tau_{wt} \propto \eta$ or $\tau_{wt} \propto \eta^2$, for the small range of viscosities tested.

Cases of a drastically different dependence of τ_{wt} on concentration were found by Western Company of Dallas, Texas (Pruitt et al.[7]). The curves of pressure drop per unit length (proportional to τ_w/D) vs flow rate for some PEO polymers in water show friction-reduction threshold stresses *decreasing* greatly with concentration increase. Since the test PEO's were of the Union Carbide Polyox WSR series, while Virk used the Union Carbide Polyox WSR N series, which have different molecular weight distributions and solution characteristics,[8] the two sets of experiments are not directly comparable.[†] However, the different character of the friction threshold concentration dependence in the Western Company data may be due to the manner of solution preparation, leading to a different size distribution of macromolecular aggregations. Pruitt[‡] of the Western Company has described the solution preparation as follows. The polymer particles were well dispersed in water with the aid of isopropanol and then allowed to solvate for just two hours without stirring. Each solution was then poured into the pipe apparatus and immediately tested. On the other hand, Toms and Virk apparently prepared their solutions with gentle mixing for long periods, and the guar gum solutions of Elata and Lehrer must have been well mixed in the closed-circuit pipe apparatus. It can be reasoned, therefore, that the polymer macromolecules were not as uniformly dispersed in the Western Company tests as they were in these other tests. One of us (Fabula) tested this conjecture by trying to duplicate the mixing technique used by the Western Company, but in a test tube with particles of Polyox WSR-301. At the end of two hours, some of the original particles, now gelatinous blobs, were still recognizable by light refraction. Thus, we shall proceed on the assumption that the Western Company results are explainable without complicating the picture of the low degree of concentration dependence obtained by other investigators.

Returning now to Fig. 1, note that if only the data for the smaller tube had been available, one might conclude that the friction reduction corresponds to merely a delayed transition from laminar to turbulent flow, rather than to an alteration of the state of the turbulent flow. This misleading interpretation is likely whenever $\tau_w = \tau_{wt}$ for the polymer under test is reached in the particular test pipe before the fully turbulent flow state of the solvent. Based on a friction coefficient of 0.01 and a Reynolds number of 5×10^3 for the start of fully turbulent flow, from Fig. 1, the corresponding wall shear stress $\tau_w{}^+$ is

$$\tau_w{}^+ \approx (0.01)\frac{\rho}{2}(5 \times 10^3)^2\left(\frac{\eta}{\rho D}\right)^2$$

Assuming typical values of $\rho = 1$ g/cc and $\eta = 0.01$ poise,

$$\tau_w{}^+ \approx \frac{12}{D^2} \quad \text{dynes/cm}^2$$

[†] The Western Company has also found at least one instance of appreciable variation between the effectiveness of different batches of the same Polyox grade. This emphasizes the importance of macromolecular characterization whenever possible, in addition to macromolecular-aggregation characterization, whose importance is evident from the above discussion.

[‡] Private communication to A. G. Fabula.

for D in centimeters. Thus, for example, if $\tau_{wt} = 12\,\text{dynes/cm}^2$ for a particular polymer, the threshold behavior will not be clearly defined unless $D \gg 1$ cm. In the recent tests by Ripken and Pilch,[9] the strikingly different effect of a polyacrylamide polymer for two values of D appears to be due to the change from $\tau_w^+ > \tau_{wt}$ to $\tau_w^+ < \tau_{wt}$.

Table I gives the values of τ_{wt} from five investigations along with relevant macromolecular parameters when available. The independence of pipe diameter, as shown with guar gum by Elata and Lehrer, is notable since it is required by any hypothesis which assumes that the friction reduction arises due to effects on the near-wall turbulence structure, as discussed later. The systematic variation of τ_{wt} with the zeroshear intrinsic viscosity $[\eta]$ is believed to be due to its macromolecular coil size significance, as seen later, rather than due to its being a measure of the relative viscosity increase per unit concentration of polymer. The relevance of $[\eta]$ was first seen experimentally in the concentration dependence of flow rate for given wall shear stress.[8]

TABLE I

τ_{wt} Values Obtained in Various Pipe Flow Experiments

τ_{wt} (dynes/cm^2)	Pipe diameter (cm)	Solvent	Polymer	$[\eta]$ (100 cc/g)	$\langle s^2 \rangle^{1/2}$ (Å)	Reference
100[a]	0.404	Monochloro-	Polymethyl-	1.3[b]	—	4
60[a]	0.129	benzene	methacrylate			
60–80	5.07–1.22	Water	Guar gum	12.0	—	3
170	3.560	Water	Polyacrylamide	—	—	9
400	0.292	Water	Poly(ethylene oxide)	0.9	300	2
90	0.292	Water	Poly(ethylene oxide)	1.8	800	2
80	0.292	Water	Poly(ethylene oxide)	3.0	800	2
5[a]	0.262	Water	Poly(ethylene oxide)	20.0[b]	2400–2700[c]	10

[a] Obtained by extrapolation of friction curves.
[b] Based on high-shear viscosities.
[c] Estimated from data of Shin.[11]

The negligible effect upon flow rate for $\tau_w < \tau_{wt}$ makes reasonable the assumption that the general structure of the turbulent flow for the dilute concentrations of interest with τ_w near to or below τ_{wt} can be taken as that of the turbulent flow of the Newtonian solvent. Thus, existing knowledge and/or reasonable interpretations of the turbulence structure in pipe and boundary layer flow of Newtonian fluids can be applied.

In a recent review of friction drag reduction, various possible alterations of the turbulent flow structure were discussed by Lumley.[12] Thus, some measurements of the mean velocity profiles in pipe flow of dilute aqueous guar gum solutions by Wells[13] are of great interest. Figure 2 shows that Wells' profiles for 500 ppm (by weight) concentration for cases of $\tau_w > \tau_{wt}$ show two drastic changes in the turbulent mean flow structure. First, there is a thickening of the viscous sublayer, shown by the higher values of $U/U_* \equiv U/\sqrt{\tau_w/\rho}$ at which the profile departs from the sublayer law: $U/U_* = U_* y/\nu$ where $\nu \equiv \eta/\rho$. Similar thickening of the viscous sublayer has been noted by Ernst[14] in pipe flow of 500 ppm of carboxymethylcellulose (CMC), a less effective additive. Second, there would appear to be a change in the "law of the wall," where for sufficiently high Reynolds number, there is an inertially dominated layer near the wall, with

$$\frac{U}{U_*} = \frac{1}{k} \ln\left(\frac{yU_*}{\nu}\right) + \text{const}$$

with $k = 0.4$ for Newtonian fluids. However, at present, it is not clear whether Wells' profile in Fig. 2 really shows that $k \approx 0.26$ or that the "buffer zone" has been greatly thickened. With the less effective CMC, Ernst found clearly that $k = 0.4$ and with little if any change to the buffer zone thickness. Tests at the same ratios of wall stress to polymer threshold stress but higher pipe Reynolds number are needed.

Our first hypothesis will be presented after first discussing the explanation of the threshold behavior offered by Virk.[2]

2. Virk's Hypothesis

In order to explain the existence of a wall-stress threshold, Virk has suggested that the onset of friction reduction corresponds to a turbulence scale (characteristic of the smallest eddies near the pipe wall) becoming small enough with respect to some macromolecular scale. Virk chooses twice the root mean square radius of gyration of the unperturbed

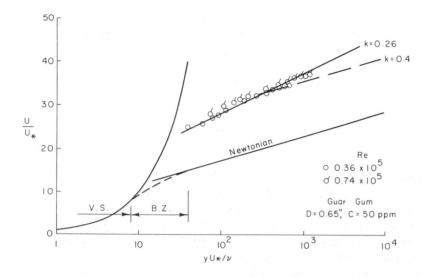

FIG. 2   Pipe flow mean velocity profile data of Wells,[13] compared with the Newtonian case.

macromolecular coil as the polymer scale and for the turbulence he chooses v/U_* as a scale characteristic of the eddies at the peak of the dissipation spectrum. Ignoring the concentration dependence of v, he has shown that $\langle s^2 \rangle^{1/2} \tau_{wt}^{1/2}$ is reasonably constant from tests in a single pipe of three† PEO polymers for which τ_{wt} varies by a factor of 5.

Since even the largest macromolecular coils have values of $\langle s^2 \rangle^{1/2}$ of the order of only a few tenths of a micron, Virk's hypothesis that the individual macromolecule is the effective particle would imply that the turbulence structure extends to surprisingly small scales. Based on present understanding of Newtonian turbulent shear flows,[15] it can be shown that the scale of the smallest significant dissipative eddies near the pipe wall is roughly v/U_*, while that of the corresponding energy containing eddies is roughly ten times larger. Thus, using Virk's data and taking v as $0.01 \text{ cm}^2/\text{sec}$, and ρ as 1 g/cc, we can evaluate the threshold value of the dimensionless ratio $2\langle s^2 \rangle^{1/2} U_* / v$ with $U_* \equiv \sqrt{\tau_w/\rho}$ (see Table II). The constancy of the ratios of the two scales in the three cases is striking, but the numerical value suggests that the individual macromolecules are too small to interfere with the turbulence

---

† This number was based on a preliminary report by Virk. See reference 2 for his extended results.

TABLE II

$\langle s^2 \rangle^{1/2}$, (Å)	τ_{wt}, (dynes/cm^2)	$2\langle s^2 \rangle^{1/2}\sqrt{\tau_w/\rho/\nu}$
300	400	0.011
800	90	0.015
800	80	0.014

structure in a particulate manner. Thus, the basis of Virk's hypothesis may be questioned, and other possible explanations are of interest.

Of course both the estimates of the coil size based on the unperturbed coil and of the smallest significant eddies are uncertain, so that the successful fitting of Virk's hypothesis to the experimental data can be justified in that way. For example the macromolecular coils are known to be elongated in shear flow,[16,17] but it would seem that only the dissipation structure would be affected in this way, and then the effect on the larger turbulence structure must still be explained in some mechanistic manner. On the other hand, a dynamically significant turbulence scale much smaller than ν/U_* might be assumed to exist in the little understood wall layer. The following hypotheses do not require the latter assumption but each requires another assumption instead.

3. A Molecular Viscoelasticity Hypothesis

Since we are mainly interested in the reduced energy dissipation, our attention can be focused on the near-wall region where for Newtonian fluids the dimensionless wall distance range is $0 < yU_*/\nu < 40$. This region contains the viscous sublayer and the buffer zone. In the former, the momentum transfer is predominantly viscous in nature, and in the latter there is concentrated a large part of the total generation and dissipation of turbulent energy. Most of the total dissipation into thermal energy occurs for $yU_*/\nu < 40$.

A significant feature of the turbulence structure is that fluid in the viscous sublayer remains there only for a finite time until it is ejected away from the wall.[18] Furthermore, it is believed that the process of turbulence generation and decay is concentrated in the deformation and distortion of the ejected fluid as it passes through the buffer zone. Thus we conjecture that the viscous sublayer fluid *and* the fluid ejected from the sublayer develop significant elasticity only when the wall shear rate $\gamma_w \equiv \tau_w/\eta$ exceeds the threshold value $\gamma_{wt} \equiv \tau_{wt}/\eta$. Thus, our first goal is to relate the values of the threshold stresses to the macro-molecular coil characteristics, since we shall assume in this first hypothesis that the macromolecules remain individually dispersed.

Two characteristic frequencies which are assumed to control the viscoelastic behavior are assigned as follows. The mean flow speed at the top of the Newtonian viscous sublayer is about $10U_*$. Thus, if the smallest energy-containing eddies of scale $10v/U_*$ acting on the top of the sublayer produce fluctuating flow in the sublayer, the corresponding linear frequency at the center of the sublayer is $f_e = \tau_w/2\eta \equiv \gamma_w/2$. On the other hand, the frequency of tumbling of the rotating macromolecules in the sublayer, according to the macromolecular coil torque equilibrium consideration used by Debye[19] and others, is $\gamma_w/4\pi$. During each rotation the coil is subject to two cycles of dilation and compression.[19,20] Thus, the frequency of this periodic deformation, f_d, is $\gamma_w/2\pi$. In summary, the macromolecular coil in the viscous sublayer is subject both to a spectrally-narrow periodic deformation characterized by a frequency f_d and to broad-band fluctuations characterized by having most energy near a frequency $f_e = \pi f_d$.

With respect to the threshold behavior, the viscoelasticity of dilute polymer solutions subjected to fluctuations superimposed on a steady shear flow becomes of interest. In the absence of any information on these properties, we make the assumption that the "viscoelastic dispersion" found in theory and experiment for $\gamma = 0$ also occurs in some form for $|\gamma| > 0$. For $\gamma = 0$, that dispersion occurs at a dimensionless frequency $\omega\tau_1 \equiv 1$, where ω is the circular frequency of the oscillatory shearing and τ_1 is the fundamental (largest) relaxation time of the macromolecular coil. According to the Zimm and Rouse theories (see Rouse and Sittel[21] and Tschoegl[22])

$$\tau_1 = a_1 \eta_s \frac{100[\eta]M}{RT} \tag{1}$$

The coefficient a_1 varies little between the theory of Rouse (for the free-draining coil) and the extended Zimm theory (for the case of arbitrary hydrodynamic interaction and excluded volume effect); we will take $a_1 = \frac{1}{2}$. η_s is the solvent viscosity; $[\eta]$ is the zeroshear intrinsic viscosity in 100 cc/g; M is the molecular weight of the polymer (assumed to be monodisperse); R is the gas constant, and T is the temperature.

It is not clear whether we should take $\omega/2\pi$ as f_e or as f_d, but the two differ only by a factor of π. Since the experiments show τ_{wt} as sharply defined, we choose f_d (the narrow-band deformation frequency) as the more likely controlling parameter. f_d is also appropriate in case the history of residence in the viscous sublayer of the fluid leaving the wall layer is important. We therefore hypothesize that the threshold condition corresponds to

$$2\pi f_d \tau_1 = 1 \qquad (2)$$

and that the two regimes of flow correspond to

$$2\pi f_d \tau_1 < 1; \qquad \tau_w < \tau_{wt}$$

$$2\pi f_d \tau_1 > 1; \qquad \tau_w > \tau_{wt}$$

where $2\pi f_d \equiv \tau_w/\eta$. The predicted threshold wall shear stress is, therefore, given by

$$\tau_{wt} = \frac{\eta}{\tau_1} = \frac{1}{100a_1} \frac{\eta}{\eta_s} \frac{RT}{[\eta]M} \qquad (3)$$

The physical basis for the τ_w threshold is hypothesized to be that only for $\tau_w > \tau_{wt}$ is there some significant but unspecified viscoelastic effect on the wall layer structure. Thus, our first hypothesis implies that a continuum theory should eventually explain the friction reduction in terms of viscoelastic properties.†

Equation (3) shows that this hypothesis, along with that of Virk, implies a dependence on concentration which is not seen in Virk's data, but may be present in those of Elata and Lehrer. Thus the concentration dependence will be ignored at present, and we rewrite Eq. (3) as

$$\tau_{wt} = \frac{1}{100a_1} \frac{RT}{[\eta]M} \qquad (3')$$

In order to compare this result with Virk's hypothesis, we use the Flory relation[22]

$$[\eta]M = \Phi(h, \varepsilon)6^{3/2}\langle s^2\rangle^{3/2}$$

where the parameter $\Phi(h, \varepsilon)$ is dependent on the macromolecular characteristics in terms of the hydrodynamic interaction parameter h and the excluded-volume expansion parameter ε. For our order of magnitude analysis, we can take $\Phi(h, \varepsilon)$ as 2×10^{21} mole^{-1} and with $a_1 = \frac{1}{2}$, we have

$$\tau_{wt} \approx \frac{RT}{10^{23} \times 6^{3/2}\langle s^2\rangle^{3/2}} \qquad (4)$$

---

† Our other hypotheses assume that particle migration and macromolecular entanglement are involved, the effects of which would be difficult to include in a continuum theory.

for τ_{wt} in dynes per centimeter squared, $\langle s^2 \rangle^{1/2}$ in centimeters, and RT in usual units. Since the corresponding form of Virk's hypothesis is

$$\tau_{wt} = \frac{\text{const}}{\langle s^2 \rangle} \tag{5}$$

the two results differ qualitatively in the power of $\langle s^2 \rangle$.

4. Comparison with Experiment

Because the measurements in Table I are for unfractionated polymers, we should not properly use them to test Eq. (4). If we suppose that the effects of an apparently broad molecular weight distribution[23] are not serious, however, we can compare Eq. (4) with Virk's data for the WSR N Polyoxes plus one case of a Polyox WSR type which we have calculated from a test by Giles.[10] Figure 3 gives a plot of Eq. (4) for $T = 25°C$,

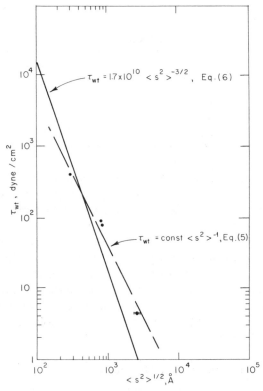

FIG. 3   Threshold wall shear stress, τ_{wt}, vs radius of gyration of PEO, compared with the two hypotheses.

τ_{wt} in dynes per centimeter squared, and $\langle s^2 \rangle^{1/2}$ in angstroms, so that Eq. (4) becomes

$$\tau_{wt} \approx \frac{8.3 \times 10^7 \times 298}{10^{23} \times 6^{3/2} \times 10^{-24} \langle s^2 \rangle^{3/2}} \approx \frac{1.7 \times 10^{10}}{\langle s^2 \rangle^{3/2}} \qquad (6)$$

Note that there are no adjustable parameters. The four data points shown are from Table I. The dashed line with a slope of -2 has the dependency predicted by Virk's hypothesis but has been fitted without regard to the dimensionless magnitude involved, as discussed earlier. The ratios of predicted to experimental τ_{wt} for the two dependencies are given in Table III. Thus the dependence on $\langle s^2 \rangle^{-1}$ implied by Virk's hypothesis allows a much better fit of the data though the magnitude suggested by the scale ratio is incompatible with present turbulence knowledge; our hypothesis with no free parameter predicts the order of magnitude of τ_{wt} but follows its variation poorly. The agreement is improved for all but the lowest $\langle s^2 \rangle^{1/2}$ value if $f_e = \pi f_d$ is used instead of f_d in Eq. (2).

TABLE III

$\langle s^2 \rangle^{1/2}$, (Å)	Eq. (6)	Eq. (5)—fitted
300	1.55	1.1
800	0.37	0.7
800	0.41	0.8
2400–2700	0.24–0.17	1.3–1.0

In order to make a better evaluation of our first hypothesis, measurements of τ_{wt} should be made with solutions of narrow fraction polymers. Measurements of the viscoelastic properties of the same solutions for conditions corresponding to the viscous sublayer are also needed.

The major weakness of our first hypothesis is the assumption that appreciable viscoelasticity can be expected of a very dilute solution of individual macromolecules. At present there seems to be no experimental or theoretical evidence that such a fluid can have appreciable elasticity. Therefore, we will consider some other hypotheses which are suggested by experimental properties of dilute polymer solutions and suspensions of particles.

5. A Molecular Entanglement Hypothesis

A simple explanation of the paradox discussed in the previous section is that the macromolecules are in fact not individually dispersed. While

for D in centimeters. Thus, for example, if $\tau_{wt} = 12\,\text{dynes/cm}^2$ for a some polymer solutions for concentrations as low as 0.045 g/liter,[24] no published reports of such aggregation for the very dilute solutions of the polymers of interest are known to us. However, Barenblat† has suggested that the Toms effect is always accompanied by the production of heterogeneities.

A possibly related phenomenon has been observed in some recent grid turbulence measurements in dilute PEO solutions.[25] When a conically shaped hot element type of turbulence sensor has been towed through a quiet tank of solution, a very few "blips" were seen on the signal, indicating passage by or impact with an occasional "blob" of gelatinous matter, still remaining from the original solution preparation. However, when the towing was done behind a grid of bars, the turbulence signal contained an unexpected high-frequency noise such as might be produced by extremely numerous blobs. It might be assumed that the blobiness is generated by the intense shear layers shed by the square bars of the grid, and that these blobs, perhaps mainly in the form of fibers, produce flow disturbances as they move past the sensor. However, the possibility also exists that the process of piling-up and washing off of gelatinous material on the rounded tip ahead of the hot film on the conical probe is a relatively smooth process in quiet flow but relatively irregular in the turbulent flow, so that the noise would be mainly due to the sensor. Work is underway to settle this question.

If these fibers do exist, it is not clear whether they would be essential to or merely by-products of the Toms effect. However, if we assume that the formation of fibers is a key aspect of the effect, two notable similarities to the friction reduction produced by dilute suspensions of wood pulp and synthetic fibers can be seen.

First, there is a qualitative similarity of the log-log curves of turbulent-flow pipe wall friction vs flow rate for wood-pulp suspensions and for dilute polymers displaying the Toms effect, in that more than one flow state is suggested by sharp breaks in the curves, as the Toms effect first increases and then diminishes.[8] However, it is not yet certain that molecular degradation is not involved when the change from increasing to decreasing percent friction reduction occurs for the polymer solutions.

Second, there is an approximate correspondence of order of magnitude of effective concentrations, which can be seen as follows. The dilute polymer solutions of interest can be described in terms of dimensionless concentrations $c[\eta]$ where c is the polymer concentration and

† G. I. Barenblat, Institute of Mechanics, Moscow, USSR, in a discussion with J. L. Lumley.

$[\eta]$ is the zeroshear intrinsic viscosity in units of $1/c$. In terms of "equivalent hydrodynamic spheres,"[26] the condition of the incipient overlap of the macromolecular coils is $c[\eta] \approx 1$. Each coil's hydrodynamic equivalent volume, though 99% solvent, is relatively gellike, and, therefore, the *volume fraction* of gellike material is roughly $c[\eta]$ for $c[\eta] < 1$, whether the coils are individually dispersed or clustered.

It is of great practical and theoretical interest that the Toms effect can be large for $c[\eta] \ll 0.1$. In turbulent Couette flow, Shin[11] has found that $c[\eta]$ can be even much less than 0.01 at the optimum concentration. However, since the optimum concentration may vary with the type of flow and may include the effects of migration, the smallness of $c[\eta] \approx 0.01$ does not necessarily mean that coil entanglement is unimportant, since contact of tumbling coils which are elongated by shear and are possibly migrating, is still perhaps fairly frequent. When contact occurs, temporary or semipermanent entanglement may result.†

Such entangled macromolecular coils presumably would be stretched into fibers by the shear flow. Thus the much larger friction reduction in suspensions of fibers than in suspensions of spheres, seems significant.[28] A 1% volume fraction of fibers can produce sizeable friction reduction, and in order for the gellike fibers which could be formed by entanglement in a polymer solution to have a 1% volume fraction, then $c[\eta]$ would be about 0.01.

Another feature of the entanglement and fiber formation hypothesis is that the fibers could introduce length or time scales to interfere with the turbulence structure away from the wall in line with Wells' mean velocity profiles.

There are a few pieces of evidence that the formation of networks of entangled macromolecules, or the deformation and possibly breakup of networks already formed, can be important in the flow of at least somewhat dilute polymer solutions. Thus, in the so-called "early" or "structural" turbulence phenomenon, some polymer solutions display in capillary flows a sudden but small rise in viscosity well before and distinct from the start of ordinary turbulent flow. In some recent work on this old but relatively unexplored idea, Ram and Tamir[29] remarked that "structural turbulence may be the result of chain deformation" and "that uncoiling of long polymer chains rotating at high speéd under severe shear conditions generates nuclei of turbulence vortices." Their careful steady-state capillary flow measurements for polyisobutylene

---

† Besides the mechanical entanglement of coil loops, hydrogen-bonding might be involved for PEO in water.[27]

polymers in several solvents showed that the onset of the effect scales with wall stress rather than with Reynolds number and that the stress *decreased* with polymer concentration. The latter dependence was attributed to the effects of macromolecular disentanglement. Their data for low concentrations of a few high molecular weight polymers suggest that the friction threshold stress and the structural turbulence onset stress conceivably could be the same for low enough concentration.

In some other capillary viscosity measurements for PEO-water and other effective solutions in concentrations such as 250 ppm the Western Company[7] has found very large entrance length corrections, beginning at stresses which could be the same as the corresponding threshold stress values. Thus, the two observations might be related to each other as follows. If elastic structures are present or are formed at the mouth of the tube, the large entrance effect would be due to the work required for their deformation. Presumably elongated fibers would be produced. As these fibers break up, an effect like the early turbulence seen by Ram and Tamir could be expected. However, the picture is inconclusive as Ram and Tamir reported negligible elastic-deformation corrections for their solutions.

An aspect of the Toms effect which could be related directly to the above is a time delay before an abrupt decrease of torque in turbulent Couette flow, reported by Shin[11] for higher than optimum concentrations.

In summary, a somewhat coherent picture is emerging from a variety of experiments which suggests that the *formation* and/or the *action* or *breakup* of *macromolecular entanglements* in polymer solution are possibly essential features of the Toms effect.

6. A Shear-Layer Modification Hypothesis

Intense unsteady shear layers are known to be a key feature of the transition from laminar to turbulent boundary layers.[30] Similar layers apparently occur in connection with the longitudinal vortices near the wall in turbulent flows in boundary layers and presumably in pipes.[18] Thus, a straightforward explanation of the Toms effect would be that the polymer additives modify the development of such layers, so as to reduce the turbulence generated by their instability and breakup.

Such a reduced turbulence generation can be imagined to arise in many ways. For example, if the state of motion of the macromolecules or clusters thereof can vary in a manner suitably related to the flow structure, then a greater dissipation of unsteady motions, as discussed by Lumley,[12] could stabilize the shear layers and/or reduce the turbulence generated by them. Such a mechanism could thicken both the viscous sublayer and the buffer zone.

This hypothesis for the Toms effect emphasizes the importance of knowing details of macromolecular configuration and motion in unsteady flows. Unfortunately, such questions are not well settled even for steady shear flow. There the deformable coil is generally pictured as elongated and tumbling. The work of Forgacs and Mason[31] with long elastomer filaments suggests that any macromolecule which happened to be fully stretched out would soon become a self-entangled ball. For the same reason, extremely elongated coils or clusters of coils would seem to be unlikely in steady shear flow. However, the transient behavior of the coil or of clusters in an unsteady, local, and intense shear layer is now also of interest and short-lived fiber configurations might be important.

The extreme diluteness of effective solutions must also be explained, and to do this, we add the assumption that local concentrations of higher than mean value are produced by migration of macromolecules and/or macromolecular clusters relative to the intense shear regions. It seems suggestive that in this way a scaling law similar to Virk's empirical result of $\langle s^2 \rangle \tau_{wt} \approx$ constant is obtained from a critical particle Reynolds number, relating particle size and vorticity gradient. This is seen as follows.

In some recent studies of the "tubular pinch" effect which is found with suspensions of *rigid* particles in Poiseuille flow,[32] a critical value of a particle Reynolds number,

$$\mathrm{Re}_p = b \left(\frac{b}{R} \right)^2 \frac{\overline{U}}{v_s}$$

is found to mark the onset of the migration. Here b is the spherical particle radius and R is the tube radius. In the form shown, the factor $(b/R)^2$ would seem to indicate the importance of relative particle and tube size. However, because of the fundamental role of vorticity gradient,† it seems that a more appropriate grouping is

$$\frac{b^3}{4} \left(\frac{4\overline{U}}{R^2} \right) \frac{1}{v_s}$$

---

† Concentration in an essentially parallel flow (such as a shear layer) must depend on migration due to inertial forces—hence the significance of the Reynolds number; the vorticity gradient is the lowest-order quantity on which this can depend, since a uniform shear cannot produce migration, by symmetry, in the absence of wall (image) effects.

since $4\bar{U}/R^2$ is the vorticity gradient in Poiseuille flow. Thus we can expect a particle Reynolds number of this form to control the migration in general flows.

With *liquid* drops in Poiseuille flow, Goldsmith and Mason[33] found migration toward the axis in agreement with theory based on deformability and the vorticity gradient. Rather than attempt to consider the deformability of macromolecular coils, we assume that the macromolecular coils (or clusters) for a homologous series of high molecular weight polymers also have a critical particle Reynolds number for the start of migration.

In order to use this parameter in the turbulent flow we reason that the characteristic magnitude of the vorticity-gradient fluctuations in the intense shear layers must be proportional to the only vorticity/length ratio we can form from the characteristic parameters of the near-wall turbulence. Therefore, $(\tau_w/\eta)/(v/U_*)$ is the vorticity gradient characteristic magnitude.† Then, if the particle radius is $n\langle s^2\rangle^{1/2}$, where n is a cluster factor, we have for the cube root of the generalized Re_p,

$$(\mathrm{Re}_p)^{1/3} = \left(\frac{2\langle s^2\rangle^{1/2}U_*}{v}\right)\left(\frac{1}{32}\frac{v}{v_s}\right)^{1/3} n$$

Thus Virk's dimensionless ratio of particle size to smallest turbulence scale times a relatively constant viscosity term and a cluster factor appears here as the cube root of a critical particle Reynolds number. Of course, any other dimensionless number characterizing the interaction of the rigid macromolecule and the near-wall turbulence structure will also lead to Virk's ratio, as long as we assume that the only characteristic flow parameters are the friction velocity and the kinematic viscosity. Thus the occurrence of Virk's result here is not surprising.

If we use the values of Virk's ratio determined earlier to calculate Re_p we obtain roughly $10^{-7} n^3$ as compared with the critical value of about 10^{-4} for rigid particles.[32] Clearly, if migration of single macromolecules is involved, the deformability of the particles must be an important factor. Since the number of macromolecules in a spherical cluster is n^3, a cluster would have to contain an unlikely number of 10^3 coils to make the Re_p values equal for rigid macromolecules.

From the known migration of deformable particles toward the axis of Poiseuille flow, we can expect migration *away* from the center of

† The numerical coefficient of unity corresponds to assuming that a jump of the magnitude of the mean vorticity at the wall occurs across a layer whose thickness is about one-tenth of the viscous sublayer thickness.

intense shear layers. This suggests that migration thickens the shear layers and thus retards their intensification.

Another way in which the shear layer intensification could be retarded is as follows. In connection with the turbulent flow of fiber suspensions, a notable phenomenon is the increased lateral component of turbulence in the presence of friction reduction.[28] Thus, if fiberlike entanglements are formed by shear layers in the Toms effect, as discussed earlier, the tumbling action of these fibers before they are fully self-entangled might produce local extra dissipation and lateral momentum diffusion near the developing shear layers.

7. Conclusions

Some hypotheses for the Toms effect and/or its threshold stress have been discussed. While a simple molecular-viscoelasticity interpretation of the threshold stress dependence upon the unperturbed diameter of the macromolecular coil was partly successful, the final picture which is suggested is one in which the key feature of the Toms is the action of clusters of macromolecules, which are formed by entanglement during flow, if not already present before flow. It is suggested that the effect of such clusters is probably concentrated near the wall in a modification of the development of the intense shear layers, which appear to play an important role in turbulent boundary layers and pipe flows.

ACKNOWLEDGMENTS

Many unpublished reports and papers in process have been reviewed in the preparation of this paper. We acknowledge our debt to those who generously provided this help, especially Professor E. W. Merrill of the Massachusetts Institute of Technology, Dr. C. Elata of the Technion in Israel, Dr. J. Harkness of Ling-Temco-Vought, G. Pruitt of Western Company, and W. B. Giles of General Electric.

REFERENCES

1. C. Elata and T. Tirosh, Frictional drag reduction, *Israel J. Tech.* **3**, 1–6 (1965).
2. P. Virk, Ph.D. Thesis, Chem. Eng. Dept., Mass. Inst. Technol., Cambridge, Massachusetts, 1966; see also P. S. Virk, E. W. Merrill, H. S. Mickley, and H. A. Smith, Critical wall shear stress for reduction of turbulent drag in pipe flows by polyethylene oxide in dilute solutions, this volume.
3. C. Elata and J. Lehrer, Frictional drag reduction: critical transition and diameter effect. Unpublished report superseded by: C. Elata, J. Lehrer, and A. Kahanovitz, Turbulent shear flow of polymer solutions, *Israel J. Tech.* **4**, 87–95 (1966).
4. B. A. Toms, Some observations on the flow of linear polymer solutions through straight tubes at large Reynolds numbers, *Proc. Intern. Congr. Rheol., Holland, 1948.* North-Holland Publ., Amsterdam, 1949.

5. J. G. Savins, Some comments on pumping requirements for non-Newtonian fluids, *J. Inst. Petrol.* **47**, 329–335 (1961).
6. J. W. Hoyt and A. G. Fabula, The effect of additives on fluid friction, *Fifth Symp. Naval Hydrodynamics, Bergen, Norway, 1964.* Office of Naval Research, Washington, D.C. (in press).
7. G. T. Pruitt, B. Rosen, and H. R. Crawford, Effect of molecular size and shape on the drag reduction of water soluble polymers. The Western Company, Res. Div. Final Rept. to David Taylor Model Basin under Contract Nonr-4306 (00) (April, 1965).
8. A. G. Fabula, The Toms phenomenon in the turbulent flow of very dilute polymer solutions, *Proc. Fourth Intern. Congr. Rheol., 1963*, Part 3, 455–479. Wiley (Interscience), New York, 1965.
9. J. F. Ripken and M. Pilch, Non-Newtonian pipe friction studies with various dilute polymer water solutions, Univ. Minnesota, St. Anthony Falls Hydraulic Lab., Project Rept. 71 (June, 1964).
10. W. B. Giles, Pipe experiments with friction-reducing additive in water, General Electric Rept. 64GL210 (1964).
11. H. Shin, Reduction of drag in turbulence by dilute polymer solutions, Ph.D. Thesis, Dept. of Chem. Eng., Mass. Inst. Technol., Cambridge, Massachusetts, 1965.
12. J. L. Lumley, The reduction of skin friction drag, *Fifth Symp. Naval Hydrodynamics, Bergen, Norway, 1964.* Office of Naval Research, Washington, D.C. (in press).
13. C. S. Wells, Anomalous turbulent flow of non-Newtonian fluids, *A.I.A.A. J.* **3**, 1800–1805 (1965).
14. W. D. Ernst, Investigation of the turbulent shear flow of dilute aqueous CMC solutions, *A.I.Ch.E. J.* **12**, 581–586 (1966).
15. A. A. Townsend, "The Structure of Turbulent Shear Flow." Cambridge Univ. Press, London and New York, 1956.
16. E. W. Merrill, Non-Newtonianism in thin liquids, *in* "Modern Chemical Engineering" (A. Acrivos, ed.), Vol. I. Reinhold, New York, 1963.
17. E. W. Merrill, K. A. Smith, H. Shin, and H. S. Mickley, Turbulent flow of polymer solutions, *Trans. Soc. Rheol.* (in press).
18. P. W. Runstadler, S. J. Kline, and W. C. Reynolds, An experimental investigation of the flow structure of the turbulent boundary layer, Stanford Univ., Stanford, California, Thermosci. Div. Rept. AFOSR-TN-5241 (1963).
19. J. Debye, The intrinsic viscosity of polymer solutions, *J. Chem. Phys.* **14**, 636-639 (1946).
20. A. Peterlin and M. Copic, Gradient dependence of the intrinsic viscosity of linear macromolecules, *J. Appl. Phys.* **27**, 434–438 (1956).
21. P. E. Rouse, Jr. and K. Sittel, Viscoelastic properties of dilute polymer solutions, *J. Appl. Phys.* **24**, 690–696 (1953).
22. N. W. Tschoegl, Influence of hydrodynamic interaction on the viscoelastic behavior of dilute polymer solutions in good solvents, *J. Chem. Phys.* **40**, 473–479 (1964).
23. H. G. Elias, Bestimmung des Molekulargewichts in der Ultrazentrifuge nach dem Archibald-Verfahren, *Angew. Chem.* **73**, 209–215 (1961).
24. A. Peterlin and D. T. Turner, Temporary network formation in shearing solutions of poly(methyl methacrylate) in Aroclor, *Polymer Letters* **3**, 517–520 (1965).
25. A. G. Fabula, An experimental study of grid turbulence in dilute high-polymer solutions, Ph.D. Thesis, Dept. of Aero. Eng., Pennsylvania State Univ., University Park, Pennsylvania, 1966.
26. C. Tanford, "Physical Chemistry of Macromolecules." Wiley, New York, 1961.

27. J. Langbein, Die Assoziation der Polyäthylenoxiden durch Wasserstoffbrücken, *Kolloid-Z.* **203**, 1–7 (1965).
28. A. J. Bobkowicz and W. H. Gauvin, The turbulent flow characteristics of model fiber suspensions, *Can. J. Chem. Eng.* **43**, 87–91 (1965).
29. A. Ram and A. Tamir, Structural turbulence in polymer solutions, *J. Appl. Polymer Sci.* **8**, 2751–2762 (1964).
30. J. T. Stuart, The production of intense shear layers by vortex stretching and convection, *Nat. Phys. Lab. Aero. Rept.* 1147 (1965).
31. O. L. Forgacs and S. G. Mason, Particle motions in sheared suspensions, X: Orbits of flexible threadlike particles, *J. Colloid Sci.* **14**, 473–491 (1959).
32. B. Shizgal, H. L. Goldsmith, and S. G. Mason, The flow of suspensions through tubes, IV: Oscillatory flow of rigid spheres, *Can. J. Chem. Eng.* **43**, 97–101 (1965).
33. H. L. Goldsmith and S. G. Mason, The flow of suspensions through tubes, I: Single spheres, rods and discs, *J. Colloid Sci.* **17**, 448–476 (1962).

Acceleration Waves in Nonlinear Materials†

BERNARD D. COLEMAN
Mellon Institute, Pittsburgh, Pennsylvania

MORTON E. GURTIN
Brown University, Providence, Rhode Island

1. Introduction

We here discuss the propagation of acceleration waves in elastic and viscoelastic materials. It is not our purpose to present the most recent and most general results, but rather to give experimenters and theorists who have not been following the subject a chance to get its flavor without having to plow through arguments involving tensor calculus and functional analysis. For this reason we consider only a one-dimensional theory which ignores both geometrical complications and thermodynamic influences,‡ we restrict our attention to waves entering regions which previously have been at rest, and we omit proofs.

2. Preliminary Definitions

Let the real line describe a homogeneous reference configuration $\mathscr{R}$ of a one-dimensional body. A motion of the body is then a function $x = x(X, t)$ giving the location x at time t of the material point which has the position X in the reference configuration. When the derivatives

$$F = \partial_X x(X, t), \qquad \dot{x} = \partial_t x(X, t), \qquad \ddot{x} = \partial_t^2 x(X, t) \qquad (2.1)$$

exist, we call them, respectively, the *deformation gradient*, the *velocity*, and the *acceleration* of X at time t. The strain $\gamma = \gamma(X, t)$ is defined by

$$\gamma = F - 1. \qquad (2.2)$$

† The preparation of this article was supported by the Air Force Office of Scientific Research under Grant AF-AFOSR-728-66 to Mellon Institute and the Office of Naval Research under Contract NONR 562(40), with Brown University.

‡ In another survey article,[1] we have outlined the theory of general three-dimensional acceleration waves in materials for which the stress depends on both the history of the strain and the history of the temperature.

In the absence of body forces, the *law of balance of momentum* asserts that

$$\frac{d}{dt}\int_{X_0}^{X_1} \dot{x}(X, t)\rho_{\mathscr{R}}\, dX = \sigma(X_1, t) - \sigma(X_0, t) \tag{2.3}$$

for all times t and every pair X_0, X_1 of points in $\mathscr{R}$. Here σ is the stress (or tension) and the constant $\rho_{\mathscr{R}}$ is the mass density in the reference configuration $\mathscr{R}$.

The *material representation of a wave*† is a smooth one-parameter family of points $Y(t)$ in $\mathscr{R}$, $-\infty < t < \infty$ such that $Y(t)$ gives the material point (labeled by its position in $\mathscr{R}$) at which the wave is to be found at time t. We assume that $x(X, t)$ is continuous for all X and t but allow certain derivatives of $x(X, t)$ to have jump discontinuities at the points $(Y(t), t)$. The *spatial representation* $y(t)$, $-\infty < t < \infty$, *of the wave* is defined by

$$y(t) = x(Y(t), t); \tag{2.4}$$

$y(t)$ is the position in space of the wave at time t.

The *wave velocity* u at time t is defined by

$$u = \frac{dy(t)}{dt} = \frac{d}{dt}x(Y(t), t); \tag{2.5}$$

u is just the rate of advance of the wave as seen by an observer at rest. We call

$$U = \frac{dY(t)}{dt} \tag{2.6}$$

the *intrinsic velocity* of the wave; U measures the velocity of propagation of the wave relative to the material. The complexity of the relation between u and U depends on how much smoothness one can assume for $x(X, t)$ as a function of X near the point $X = Y(t)$.

An *acceleration wave* is a wave across which the acceleration, strain gradient, and velocity gradient suffer jump discontinuities, but across which the velocity and strain are continuous. These are the main smoothness requirements. At times it will be obvious that additional smoothness hypotheses are needed; we will not mention these explicitly.

---

† What we here call a wave is often called a "wave front." Its analog in three-dimensional theories is sometimes called a "singular surface."

For simplicity we here consider only acceleration waves which since time $t = 0$ have been propagating into a region which previously had been at rest in the reference configuration $\mathscr{R}$; i.e., we suppose that $U(t) > 0$ and that for $X \geqslant Y(t)$ and $t \geqslant 0$

$$x(X, \tau) = X, \qquad -\infty < \tau \leqslant t. \tag{2.7}$$

It follows from (2.5)–(2.7) that in the present circumstances

$$u(t) = U(t), \qquad t \geqslant 0. \tag{2.8}$$

Also, by (2.7), the acceleration immediately ahead of the wave vanishes. We call the acceleration

$$a(t) = \lim_{X \to Y(t)^-} \ddot{x}(X, t) \tag{2.9}$$

immediately behind the wave the *amplitude* of the wave. We say that the wave is *expansive* if $a < 0$ and *compressive* if $a > 0$. Although our terminology may seem to indicate that we have in mind longitudinal motion of an isotropic cylinder, with minor modifications the theory presented here may be applied also to pure shear waves in incompressible isotropic media.†

3. Waves in Elastic Materials

In an elastic material‡ the present strain γ determines the present stress σ:

$$\sigma = \hat{\sigma}(\gamma). \tag{3.1}$$

The numbers

$$E = \left.\frac{d\hat{\sigma}}{d\gamma}\right|_{\gamma=0}, \qquad \tilde{E} = \left.\frac{d^2\hat{\sigma}}{d\gamma^2}\right|_{\gamma=0}, \tag{3.2}$$

are called the *tangent modulus* and *second-order modulus* at zero strain.

THEOREM 1. *For an acceleration wave entering an elastic material at rest in its reference configuration, the velocity U is a constant given by*

$$U = \sqrt{\frac{E}{\rho_{\mathscr{R}}}}, \tag{3.3}$$

---

† In Ref. 2 (Coleman *et al.*[2]) the reader will find examples of circumstances in which the behavior of three-dimensional bodies is described by the one-dimensional theory.

‡ The elastic materials considered here may be either solids or fluids.

and the amplitude a has the following explicit dependence on t:

$$a(t) = \frac{a(0)}{1 + va(0)t}, \qquad v = \frac{\tilde{E}}{2UE}. \qquad (3.4)$$

Equation (3.3) is a special case of a general result of Hadamard[3][†]; Eq. (3.4) was derived by Thomas[17] for elastic fluids. More recently, Green[5] has shown that in the three-dimensional theory an equation of the form (3.4) holds for all plane acceleration waves in homogeneously strained isotropic elastic materials. His results enable one to calculate v given the stress-strain relation, the deformation gradient ahead of the wave, the direction of propagation, and the direction of the amplitude vector.

COROLLARY TO THEOREM 1. *If* $\begin{Bmatrix} \tilde{E} < 0 \\ \tilde{E} > 0 \end{Bmatrix}$, *then the amplitude of* $\begin{Bmatrix} a\ compressive \\ an\ expansive \end{Bmatrix}$ *acceleration wave in an elastic material tends to infinity in a finite time, while the amplitude of* $\begin{Bmatrix} an\ expansive \\ a\ compressive \end{Bmatrix}$ *wave tends to zero as* $t \to \infty$. *If* $\tilde{E} = 0$, *then all acceleration waves propagate with constant amplitude.*

4. Waves in Linearly Viscoelastic Materials

The linear theory of viscoelasticity is based on the constitutive relation

$$\sigma(t) = \sigma_0 + G(0)\gamma(t) + \int_0^\infty G'(s)\gamma(t - s)\,ds, \qquad (4.1)$$

where $G(s)$, $0 \leqslant s < \infty$, is a material function called the *stress-relaxation function*, $G'(s) = dG(s)/ds$, and σ_0 is the residual stress, i.e., the stress the material exhibits when left at equilibrium in the reference configuration. It is clear from (4.1) that $G(0)$ governs the instantaneous response to changes in strain. Intuition suggests that in linear viscoelasticity the velocity of singular surfaces should be given by a formula completely analogous to that familiar in linear elasticity, with the initial value $G(0)$ of the stress relaxation function playing the role of the elastic modulus. That this is indeed the case is borne out by the next theorem.

† See also Truesdell.[4]

THEOREM 2. *For an acceleration wave entering a linearly viscoelastic material, the velocity U is a constant given by*

$$U = \sqrt{\frac{G(0)}{\rho_{\mathscr{R}}}}, \tag{4.2}$$

and the amplitude a has the following explicit dependence on t:

$$a(t) = a(0)e^{-\mu t}, \qquad \mu = -\frac{G'(0)}{2G(0)}. \tag{4.3}$$

A proof of this theorem is given by Coleman and Gurtin.[6]

COROLLARY TO THEOREM 2. *If we assume, as is natural, that*

$$G(0) > 0, \qquad G'(0) < 0, \tag{4.4}†$$

then in a linearly viscoelastic material $a(t) \to 0$ as $t \to \infty$ regardless of whether the wave is compressive or expansive.

Due to the linearity of the field equations of linear viscoelasticity theory, (4.2) and (4.3) are valid even when the material ahead of the wave is undergoing an arbitrary motion. Of course, $a(t)$ then represents not the acceleration behind the wave, but rather the jump in the acceleration across the wave.

Sips,[9] Lee and Kanter,[10] Bland,[11] and Chu[12] have exhibited explicit solutions of the dynamical equations for linearly viscoelastic materials showing shock waves. In their solutions the velocity and strength of the shock obey (4.2), (4.3). It is a trivial matter to construct from their results new solutions showing acceleration waves which, of course, also obey (4.2), (4.3). That the damping of shock waves and acceleration waves is of the same form in linear viscoelasticity is a consequence of the linearity of the field equations used in that theory.‡

5. Waves in Simple Materials with Memory

In a general simple material, instead of (4.1) we have

$$\sigma(t) = \mathop{\mathfrak{I}}_{s=0}^{\infty} (\gamma^t(s)), \tag{5.1}$$

† Coleman[7] has shown that $G(0) \geqslant 0$ is a consequence of the second law of thermodynamics. We do not consider here the case $G(0) = 0$, for it yields $U = 0$. Gurtin and Herrera[8] have shown that a material with $G'(0) > 0$ would not be dissipative in the sense of their definition (1.4). If $G'(0) = 0$ then, of course, $a(t)$ is constant.

‡ Fisher and Gurtin[13] have shown that in a linearly viscoelastic material waves of all orders obey the same laws of propagation.

or, with fewer embellishments,

$$\sigma(t) = \mathfrak{T}(\gamma^t), \tag{5.2}$$

where γ^t, defined by

$$\gamma^t(s) = \gamma(t - s), \qquad 0 \leqslant s < \infty, \tag{5.3}$$

is a function called the *strain history* up to time t, and $\mathfrak{T}$ is a functional (which certainly need not be linear) of γ^t. We make no assumptions about the functional $\mathfrak{T}$ other than a smoothness hypothesis called the "principle of fading memory."

We define the *norm* $\|\gamma^t\|$ *of a history* γ^t by

$$\|\gamma^t\|^2 = |\gamma(t)|^2 + \int_0^\infty |h(s)\gamma(t - s)|^2 \, ds, \tag{5.4}$$

where $h(s)$ is a fixed influence function, i.e., a continuous, monotone-decreasing, square integrable function. The set of all histories with finite norm forms a Hilbert space. We assume that our constitutive functional $\mathfrak{T}$ is defined and twice continuously differentiable, in the sense of Fréchet, on this space. Therefore, in particular, $\mathfrak{T}$ is continuous in the sense that the stresses $\sigma_1 = \mathfrak{T}(\gamma_1^t)$ and $\sigma_2 = \mathfrak{T}(\gamma_2^t)$ resulting from two different strain histories γ_1^t and γ_2^t are close to each other whenever $\|\gamma_1^t - \gamma_2^t\|$ is small. By (5.4), $\|\gamma_1^t - \gamma_2^t\|$ will be small provided: (a) $\gamma_1(t)$ is close to $\gamma_2(t)$ at time t, and (b) the weighted average

$$\int_0^\infty h^2(s)|\gamma_1(t - s) - \gamma_2(t - s)|^2 \, ds$$

is small. Condition (a) expresses the requirement that the material respond to *instantaneous* changes in strain at the present time t. Condition (b) is the essence of the assumption of *fading memory*.† Since $h(s)$ is monotone-decreasing, the continuity of $\mathfrak{T}$ implies that what was done to the material in the recent past (small s) is more important than what was done in the distant past (large s).

Both the elastic material of Section 3 and the linear viscoelastic material of Section 4 fall as special cases within our present framework. The next theorem, which is a special case of a more general result of Coleman and Noll,[15] shows that every functional in our theory is approximated by some functional of linear viscoelasticity in the limit of small deformations.

---

† This mathematical description of fading memory is due to Coleman and Noll.[14]

THEOREM 3. *Corresponding to each nonlinear material whose constitutive functional $\mathfrak{T}$ has fading memory there exists a linearly viscoelastic material, with relaxation function $G(s)$, having the following property. If $\sigma(t) = \mathfrak{T}(\gamma^t)$ and $\varepsilon = \|\gamma^t\|$, then*

$$\sigma(t) = \sigma_0 + G(0)\gamma(t) + \int_0^\infty G'(s)\gamma(t - s)\,ds + O(\varepsilon^2), \qquad as \quad \varepsilon \to 0. \quad (5.5)$$

An elementary proof of this theorem in its present one-dimensional form is given by Coleman *et al.*[2] Theorem 3 associates with every general functional $\mathfrak{T}$ of our theory a function $G(s)$. We call $G(s)$ the *relaxation function corresponding to the tangent linearly viscoelastic material.*

Consider now the special history $\overset{*}{\gamma}{}^t$ defined as follows:

$$\overset{*}{\gamma}{}^t(s) = \begin{cases} \gamma, & \text{for} \quad s = 0, \\ 0, & \text{for} \quad s > 0. \end{cases} \quad (5.6)$$

Thus $\overset{*}{\gamma}{}^t$ gives the history of a material which has just experienced a strain impulse of amount γ and which previously had been at rest in its reference configuration. The stress $\sigma = \mathfrak{T}(\overset{*}{\gamma}{}^t)$ at time t corresponding to the history $\overset{*}{\gamma}{}^t$ depends only on the amount γ of the strain impulse, i.e.,

$$\sigma = \hat{\sigma}(\gamma). \quad (5.7)$$

We call (5.7) the *instantaneous stress-strain relation* for our material. It is a consequence of our smoothness hypotheses on $\mathfrak{T}$ that this instantaneous stress-strain relation exists and is twice continuously differentiable. In analogy to (3.2) we call the derivatives

$$E = \left.\frac{d\hat{\sigma}}{d\gamma}\right|_{\gamma=0}, \qquad \tilde{E} = \left.\frac{d^2\hat{\sigma}}{d\gamma^2}\right|_{\gamma=0}, \quad (5.8)$$

respectively, the *instantaneous tangent modulus* and the *instantaneous second-order modulus* at zero strain. It is not difficult to show that if $G(s)$ is the relaxation function corresponding to the tangent linearly viscoelastic material, then

$$E = G(0). \quad (5.9)$$

The next theorem† shows that our smoothness assumption on the nonlinear functional $\mathfrak{T}$ suffices to yield explicit formulae for the velocity and amplitude of the wave.

---

† Coleman and Gurtin.[6] For the case in which the response functional $\mathfrak{T}$ can be expanded in a series of multiple integrals an equivalent result was obtained independently by Varley.[16] Varley also obtained the corresponding results for cylindrical and spherical waves.

THEOREM 4. *For a simple material with fading memory, the velocity U of an acceleration wave propagating into a region which has always been at rest in its reference configuration is given by*

$$U = \sqrt{\frac{G(0)}{\rho_{\mathscr{R}}}}, \tag{5.10}$$

and the amplitude a has the following explicit dependence on t:

$$d(t) = \frac{\lambda}{(-1 + \lambda/a(0))e^{\mu t} + 1}, \qquad \mu = -\frac{G'(0)}{2G(0)}, \quad \lambda = \frac{G'(0)U}{\tilde{E}}. \tag{5.11}$$

Thus U, μ, and λ are constants depending on only the density $\rho_{\mathscr{R}}$, the instantaneous second-order modulus $\tilde{E}$, and the initial value G(0) and slope G'(0) of the relaxation function corresponding to the tangent linearly viscoelastic material.

This theorem was proven by Coleman and Gurtin.[6] If we let $G'(0) \to 0$, (5.11) reduces to (3.4); on the other hand, if $\tilde{E} \to 0$, (5.11) reduces to (4.3). Hence we recover as limit cases the corresponding results for elasticity and linear viscoelasticity theory.

For the remainder of this discussion let us assume that

$$G(0) > 0, \qquad G'(0) < 0, \qquad \tilde{E} \neq 0. \tag{5.12}$$

We call an acceleration wave *weak* if

$$\left| \frac{a(0)}{\lambda} \right| < 1, \tag{5.13}$$

and *strong* if

$$\left| \frac{a(0)}{\lambda} \right| > 1. \tag{5.14}$$

For weak waves (5.11) implies the following asymptotic result:

$$\frac{a(t)}{a(0)} = e^{-\mu t}[1 + O(\varepsilon)], \qquad \text{as} \quad \varepsilon = \left| \frac{a(0)}{\lambda} \right| \to 0. \tag{5.15}$$

As we observed in the Corollary to Theorem 2, $a(t) \to 0$ as $t \to \infty$ for linearly viscoelastic materials, regardless of the sign of $a(0)$. The gap between this observation and that in the Corollary to Theorem 1 for nonlinear but elastic materials is filled by the following theorem which is valid for all simple materials with fading memory, and which follows immediately from an analysis of the function on the right in $(5.11)_1$.

THEOREM 5. *Suppose* $\left\{ \begin{matrix} \tilde{E} < 0 \\ \tilde{E} > 0 \end{matrix} \right\}$; *if the wave is weak or* $\left\{ \begin{matrix} expansive \\ compressive \end{matrix} \right\}$

then $a(t) \to 0$ *as* $t \to \infty$. *If the wave is strong and* $\left\{ \begin{matrix} compressive \\ expansive \end{matrix} \right\}$, *then* $a(t) \to \infty$ *in a finite time. If* $a(0) = \lambda$ *then* $a(t) \equiv a(0)$.

In other words, it follows from (5.12) that if the amplitude is sufficiently small or if the amplitude has the same sign as the instantaneous second-order modulus, then an acceleration wave entering a homogeneous region at rest is gradually damped out; if, however, the wave is strong and the sign of the amplitude is opposite to that of the instantaneous second-order modulus, then the wave blows up, i.e., achieves an infinite amplitude in a finite time, which may mean that a shock wave is produced. We note that the presence of internal damping, manifested by a strictly negative value of $G'(0)$, does *not* imply that *all* singular surfaces moving into a homogeneous region must be damped out.

A qualitative, experimental verification of Theorem 5 is obtained for a gas whenever one generates a shock wave from a sound impulse in a shock tube. The motion of a gas in a shock tube can be assumed to be longitudinal. For most gases, including ideal gases, $\tilde{E} < 0$; therefore, Theorem 5 tells us that an acceleration wave in a tube should grow into a shock wave only if it is compressive, and this is precisely what is observed. This theorem also tells us that the shock wave should not form unless the acceleration wave is strong, i.e., unless $|a(t)|$ is initially greater than the *critical amplitude* $|\lambda|$. We do not know whether this critical amplitude has been measured precisely, but surely it exists, otherwise every sudden burst of sound, no matter how faint, as it moves down a long tube of air would eventually grow into a shock wave.

REFERENCES

1. B. D. Coleman and M. E. Gurtin, Thermodynamics and wave propagation, *Rept. 100. Contract NONR 562(10)*, Div. Appl. Math., Brown Univ., Providence, Rhode Island (April, 1965). To appear in the *Quart. Appl. Math.*
2. B. D. Coleman, M. E. Gurtin, and I. Herrera R., *Arch. Rational Mech. Anal.* **19**, 1–19 (1965).
3. J. Hadamard, *Bull. Soc. Math. France* **29**, 50–60 (1901).
4. C. Truesdell, *Arch. Rational Mech. Anal.* **8**, 263–296 (1961).
5. W. A. Green, *Arch. Rational Mech. Anal.* **16**, 79–88 (1964).
6. B. D. Coleman and M. E. Gurtin, *Arch. Rational Mech. Anal.* **19**, 239–265 (1965).
7. B. D. Coleman, *Arch. Rational Mech. Anal.* **17**, 230–254 (1964).
8. M. E. Gurtin and I. Herrera R., *Quart. Appl. Math.* **22**, 360–364 (1964).
9. R. Sips, *J. Polymer Sci.* **6**, 285 (1951).
10. E. H. Lee and I. Kanter, *J. Appl. Phys.* **24**, 1115–1122 (1953).

11. D. R. Bland, *Proc. Conf. Properties Materials at High Rates of Strain, Inst. Mech. Eng. (London)* **56** (1957).
12. B. T. Chu, Stress waves in isotropic viscoelastic materials 1, *ARPA Rept., Div. Eng., Brown Univ.,* Providence, Rhode Island (March, 1962).
13. G. M. C. Fisher and M. E. Gurtin, *Quart. Appl. Math.* **23**, 257–263 (1965).
14. B. D. Coleman and W. Noll, *Arch. Rational Mech. Anal.* **6**, 355–370 (1960).
15. B. D. Coleman and W. Noll, *Rev. Modern Phys.* **33**, 239–249 (1961).
16. E. Varley, *Arch. Rational Mech. Anal.* **19**, 215–225 (1965).
17. T. Y. Thomas, *J. Math. Mech.* **6**, 455–469 (1957).

The Speed of Propagation of Signals in Viscoelastic Materials

JOSE BARBERAN F. and ISMAEL HERRERA R.

Instituto de Geofísica
Universidad Nacional de México
Mexico City, Mexico

1. Introduction

Recent work on the propagation of wavefronts in materials with memory by Herrera and Gurtin,[1] Coleman *et al.*,[2] Coleman and Gurtin[3,4] and Varley[5] has shown that the dynamic equations for such materials exhibit many of the properties of hyperbolic partial differential equations.

However, it seems that so far this fact has not been exploited in the solution of problems. The only case reported in the literature of which I am aware are some papers by Glanx and Lee,[6] and Lee and Kanter[7] in which they used the method of characteristics to solve some problems. But this was done only for a very special type of strain-stress relations for which it was possible to reduce the equations of motion to partial differential equations of hyperbolic type without memory.

Thus, it is natural to try to formulate a general mathematical theory of functional partial differential equations of hyperbolic type which would include as a particular case the equations of motion for materials with memory.

Within this program, I have recently formulated a theory for nonlinear systems of functional partial differential equations of hyperbolic type in two variables and proved existence and uniqueness of solution in a domain of determinacy.

To extend such a theory to equations for functions in four variables (three spatial variables and time) does not seem to be an easy task. Therefore, I have recently restricted my attention to linear systems. One of the simplest problems that may be considered refers to questions of uniqueness. In this paper, attention will be restricted to the equations of motion for the linear dynamic theory of viscoelasticity.

Uniqueness questions for quasi-static linear viscoelasticity have been extensively studied.[8-10] However, the equations of quasi-static viscoelasticity differ from those of dynamic viscoelasticity in one essential

175

respect: for any given past history the former are elliptic while the latter are hyperbolic. Correspondingly, the well-posed problems in both cases are different.

Initial boundary value problems for the dynamic theory have already been investigated.[11,12] On the other hand, Cauchy's initial value problems apparently have not been investigated at all, in spite of the fact that this type of problem is specially relevant in connection with hyperbolic equations.

Uniqueness questions for Cauchy problems are connected with the determination of appropriate domains of determinacy whose knowledge in turn gives information about the speed of propagation of viscoelastic signals, because the speed with which the boundary of a domain of determinacy moves is a bound for the speed of propagation of signals. If the domain of determinacy is maximum in some sense, then the speed with which its boundary moves equals the speed of propagation of viscoelastic signals.

The purpose of this paper is to report a uniqueness theorem for a Cauchy's initial value problem in the domain of determinacy defined by the speed of propagation of acceleration waves.[1]

When formulating Cauchy's initial value problems for equations with memory, not only the initial values of displacements and velocities must be given, but the whole past history must be given as well. Then, the problem consists in determining a solution in the domain of determinacy, having the given past history.

Roughly speaking, a theorem reported in this paper shows that if the past history of a material is prescribed in a region R_0 of E^3, then there is at most one solution of the equations of motion in any domain obtained by shrinking R_0 at a speed which is everywhere larger than the greatest speed of propagation of acceleration waves. This tends to give support to the widespread suspicion that the speed of propagation of signals equals the maximum speed of propagation of weak discontinuities; a suspicion which is also supported by what is known in some other fields such as the theory of elasticity.[13]

It is assumed that the elastic tensor is initially symmetric and initially positive definite but anisotropic and inhomogeneous. Another good feature of the theorem is that it does not assume that the elastic tensor is time translation invariant, an assumption which has been used in almost every previous discussion of uniqueness questions.

The method used to prove the theorem mentioned above, with slight modifications, can be applied to boundary value problems. Therefore, it has also been used to generalize in one direction a result originally due to Eldestein and Gurtin (first uniqueness theorem of Eldestein and Gurtin[11]) by removing the requirement that the elastic tensor be time translation invariant.

2. Notation

Let $\mathbf{x}$ be a point of the Euclidean space E^3 and t the time. Let R_0 be a compact region of E^3 whose boundary is R_0. Even more, we assume that R_0 is the closure of a normal domain, i.e., we assume that R_0 is closed and bounded in E^3 and that the divergence theorem can be applied in R_0. B_u and B_τ will be complementary subsets of ∂R_0, i.e.,

$$\partial R_0 = B_u \cup B_\tau \qquad B_u \cap B_\tau = \phi$$

We use index notation, and Latin indices will run from 1 to 3 unless otherwise explicitly stated. Summation will be understood over repeated indices.

For a function $f(\mathbf{x}, t)$ we use the notation

$$\underbrace{f^{(n)}_{,ij\cdots k}}_{m\text{-indices}} (\mathbf{x}, t) = \frac{\partial^{m+n} f(\mathbf{x}, t)}{\partial x_i\, \partial x_j \cdots \partial x_k\, \partial t^n}$$

We define the norm of a tensor $A_{ij\cdots k}$ by

$$\|\mathbf{A}\|^2 = \|A_{ij\cdots k}\|^2 = A_{ij\cdots k} A_{ij\cdots k} \qquad (2.1a)$$

Observe that if $A_{ij\cdots k}$ and $B_{ij\cdots k\cdots n}$ are two tensors and

$$C_{l\cdots n} = A_{ij\cdots k} B_{ij\cdots kl\cdots n}$$

then

$$\|\mathbf{C}\| \leqslant \|\mathbf{A}\|\, \|\mathbf{B}\| \qquad (2.1b)$$

The Cartesian components of the relaxation tensor will be denoted by $G_{ijpq}(\mathbf{x}, t, \tau)$; they are assumed to be in general a function of $\mathbf{x}, t, \tau$ so that the subject of our discussion will be an inhomogeneous, anisotropic solid whose stress-strain relation is not restricted to be time translation invariant, $u_i(\mathbf{x}, t)$ will be the Cartesian components of the displacement vector; $\tau_{ij}(\mathbf{x}, t)$ the Cartesian components of the stress tensor; $\rho(\mathbf{x})$ the mass density; and $C_{ijpq}(\mathbf{x}, t) \equiv G_{ijpq}(\mathbf{x}, t, \tau)$ the "initial value" of G_{ijpq}.

We denote by $\xi = (\mathbf{x}, t) = (x_1, x_2, x_3, t)$ a point in the space-time $(E^3 \times (-\infty, \infty))$. All integrals will be in the four-dimensional space-time in which $d\xi$ denotes the element of integration. The character of the integrals (volume or surface integral) will be denoted by a subindex under the integral sign.

The symbols $\dot{G}_{ijpq}$ and $\bar{G}_{ijpq}$ are defined by

$$\dot{G}_{ijpq}(\mathbf{x}, t, \tau) = \frac{\partial}{\partial t} G_{ijpq}(\mathbf{x}, t, \tau) \tag{2.2}$$

$$\bar{G}_{ijpq}(\mathbf{x}, t, \tau) = \frac{\partial}{\partial \tau} G_{ijpq}(\mathbf{x}, t, \tau) \tag{2.3}$$

We say that $G_{ijpq}(\mathbf{x}, t, \tau)$ is initially symmetric when

$$C_{ijpq}(\mathbf{x}, t) = C_{pqij}(\mathbf{x}, t) \tag{2.4}$$

and initially positive definite if

$$C_{ijpq}(\mathbf{x}, t)a_{ij}a_{pq} > 0 \tag{2.5}$$

whenever the symmetric part of a_{ij} is nonzero.

Let $T > 0$; for every $t \in [0, T]$, $E^3 \times [t, t]$ is a three-dimensional Euclidean space immersed in the four-dimensional space-time. For every $t \in [0, T]$ we consider a compact region $R(t) \subset E^3 \times [t, t]$ which we assume to be the closure of a normal domain.

Let

$$V(t) = \bigcup_{\tau=0}^{\tau=t} R(\tau) \tag{2.6}$$

and $S^*(t)$ the boundary of $V(t)$ in the space-time. We assume that

(a) $V(t)$ is the closure of a normal domain (compact),

(b) $R(0) = R_0 \times [0, 0]$,

and adopt the following notation:

$$S_1(t) = R(0)$$

$$S_2(t) = \text{closure of } \{S^*(t) \cap [E^3 \times (0, t)]\}$$

$$S_3(t) = R(t)$$

Observe that

$$S^*(t) = S_1(t) \cup S_2(t) \cup S_3(t)$$

The unit outer normal vector to $S^*(t)$ will be denoted by $n_\alpha(\mathbf{x}, \tau)$ ($\alpha = 1, 2, 3, 4$) at every point $(\mathbf{x}, \tau) \in S^*(t)$. It is assumed to be defined and continuous in $S_2(T)$. It must be understood that n_i ($i = 1, 2, 3$) are the spatial components while n_4 is the time component.

The above assumptions imply that

$$n_i = 0 \qquad n_4 = -1 \qquad \text{on} \quad S_1(t) \tag{2.7}$$

$$n_i = 0 \qquad n_4 = 1 \qquad \text{on} \quad S_3(t) \tag{2.8}$$

We consider two types of domains $V(T)$. One type will be when $V(T)$ is a "hypercylinder" and the other one will be when $V(T)$ is a "conoid."

We say that $V(T)$ is a hypercylinder if

$$n_4(\mathbf{x}, t) = 0 \qquad \text{for every} \quad (\mathbf{x}, t) \in S_2(T) \tag{2.9}$$

In this case $S_2(T) = R_0 \times [0, T]$ and the spatial components n_i of n_α ($\alpha = 1, 2, 3, 4$) constitute the outer unit normal vector to R_0.

In the case when $V(T)$ is a conoid we assume that $R(t)$ shrinks with time, i.e.,

$$R(t') \subset R(t) \qquad \text{whenever} \quad t' > t$$

We require even more than that. It is assumed that

$$n_4(\mathbf{x}, \tau) > 0 \qquad \text{whenever} \quad (\mathbf{x}, \tau) \in S_2(T) \tag{2.10}$$

Therefore, when $V(T)$ is a conoid there is a k $(0 < k < 1)$ such that

$$n_4(\mathbf{x}, \tau) > k \qquad \text{whenever} \quad (\mathbf{x}, \tau) \in S_2 \tag{2.11}$$

because n_4 is continuous on $S_2(T)$ which is compact.

Herrera and Gurtin[1] have established that the speed of propagation v of acceleration waves in any direction $\mathbf{e}$ satisfies the eigenvalue problem

$$(C_{ijkl}e_j e_l - \rho v^2 \, \delta_{ik})a_k = 0 \tag{2.12}$$

where $\mathbf{a}$ is some vector ($\mathbf{a} \neq 0$). The possible speeds, solutions of (2.12), will be denoted by v_1, v_2, v_3. It will be assumed that

$$0 < v_1 \leqslant v_2 \leqslant v_3 \tag{2.13}$$

3. Statement of the Problem

We consider the field equations of the linear theory of viscoelasticity

$$\tau_{ij,j}(\mathbf{x}, t) - \rho(\mathbf{x})u_i^{(2)}(\mathbf{x}, t) + F_i(\mathbf{x}, t) = 0 \tag{3.1}$$

in the region $V(T)$ where u_i is the displacement field and F_i the body forces.

The stress relation is

$$\tau_{ij}(\mathbf{x}, t) = C_{ijpq}(\mathbf{x}, t)u_{p,q}(\mathbf{x}, t) - \int_{-\infty}^{t} \bar{G}_{ijpq}(\mathbf{x}, t, \tau)u_{p,q}(\mathbf{x}, \tau) \, d\tau \tag{3.2}$$

Given $\mathbf{u}(\mathbf{x}, t)$ defined in $V(T) \cup P$ and C^2 in $V(T)$, we give the name "initial velocity" to a function $S(\mathbf{x})$ defined by

$$S(\mathbf{x}) = \mathbf{u}^{(1)}(\mathbf{x}, 0+) \qquad \text{on} \quad R_0 \tag{3.3a}$$

and "past history" to the function $\pi(\mathbf{x}, t)$ which is the restriction to P of the function $\mathbf{u}(\mathbf{x}, t)$, i.e.,

$$\pi(\mathbf{x}, t) = \mathbf{u}(\mathbf{x}, t) \qquad \text{on} \quad P \tag{3.3b}$$

where the "past" P is the set

$$P = R_0 \times (-\infty, 0] \tag{3.4}$$

When $V(T)$ is a hypercylinder, given the functions $u_i^*(\mathbf{x}, t)$ defined on B_u and $T_i(\mathbf{x}, t)$ defined on B_τ we say that a function $\mathbf{u}(\mathbf{x}, t)$ defined on $V(T) \cup P$ meets the boundary conditions if

$$\mathbf{u}(\mathbf{x}, t) = \mathbf{u}^*(\mathbf{x}, t) \qquad (\mathbf{x}, t) \in B_u \times [0, T] \tag{3.5}$$

$$\tau_{ij}(\mathbf{x}, t)n_j = T_i(\mathbf{x}, t) \qquad (\mathbf{x}, t) \in B_\tau \times [0, T] \tag{3.6}$$

In what follows we assume that

(a) $\rho(\mathbf{x})$ is continuous and positive in R_0.
(b) $\pi(\mathbf{x}, t) \in C^2$ and is such that

$$\int_{-\infty}^{0} \bar{G}_{ijpq}(\mathbf{x}, t, \tau)\pi_{p,q}(\mathbf{x}, \tau)\, d\tau$$

exists and belongs to C^2 on $V(T)$.
(c) $G_{ijpq}(\mathbf{x}, t, \tau) \in C^2$ in the closed region of E^5 where $(\mathbf{x}, t) \in V(T)$ and $0 \leqslant \tau \leqslant t$.
(d)

$$G_{ijkl}(\mathbf{x}, t, \tau) = G_{jikl}(\mathbf{x}, t, \tau) = G_{ijlk}(\mathbf{x}, t, \tau) \tag{3.7}$$

whenever $(\mathbf{x}, t) \in V(T)$ and $0 \leqslant \tau \leqslant t$.

As is well known, in the linear theory of viscoelasticity the symmetries (3.7) are satisfied under very general conditions. Indeed, the relation

$$G_{ijkl} = G_{jikl}$$

follows from the symmetry of the stress tensor, while the relation

$$G_{ijkl} = G_{ijlk}$$

is a consequence of the principle of objectivity which implies that the stress tensor is a functional of the symmetric part of $u_{i,j}$ only.

Given $G_{ijpq}(\mathbf{x}, t, \tau)$ in the region where $(\mathbf{x}, t) \in P \cup V(T)$, $\tau \leqslant t$, $\rho(\mathbf{x})$ in R_0, $\pi(\mathbf{x}, t)$ in P, $\mathbf{S}(\mathbf{x})$ in R_0, $\mathbf{F}$ in $V(T)$, we consider two different types of problems.

A. THE MIXED PROBLEMS OF DYNAMIC VISCOELASTICITY

When $V(T)$ is a hypercylinder, given the functions $u_i{}^*$ and T_i, we say that $\mathbf{u}(\mathbf{x}, t)$ defined in $V(T) \cup P$ is a solution of the "mixed problem of viscoelasticity" if:

(a) $\mathbf{u}(\mathbf{x}, t) \in C^2$ in $V(T)$.

(b) $\mathbf{u}, \mathbf{F}, G_{ijpq}$, and ρ satisfy the field equation (3.1) in $V(T)$. In these equations τ_{ij} is interpreted as a shorthand writing defined by (3.2).

(c) The past history and initial velocity of $\mathbf{u}$ are given by (3.3).

(d) $\mathbf{u}$ and τ_{ij} satisfy the boundary conditions (3.5) and (3.6), respectively.

B. CAUCHY'S INITIAL VALUE PROBLEM FOR DYNAMIC VISCOELASTICITY

When $V(T)$ is a conoid we say that $\mathbf{u}(\mathbf{x}, t)$ defined in $P \cup V(T)$ is a solution of "Cauchy's initial value problem for viscoelasticity" if $\mathbf{u}$ satisfies (a), (b), and (c) of Section A.

We are now in a position to state the theorems.

THEOREM 1. *Assume that the relaxation tensor $G_{ijpq}(\mathbf{x}, t, \tau)$ is initially symmetric and initially positive definite. Then the mixed problem of viscoelasticity has at most one solution in $V(T) \cup P$.*

THEOREM 2. *Assume that the relaxation tensor $G_{ijpq}(\mathbf{x}, t, \tau)$ is initially symmetric and initially positive definite. Let the unit normal vector be given by*

$$\mathbf{n} = \lambda(e_1, e_2, e_3, c) \tag{3.8}$$

on $S_2(T)$, where $\mathbf{e}$ is a unit vector (normal to $R(t)$) and $\lambda > 0$ is a normalizing factor.

Then, if

$$c > v_3 \geqslant v_2 \geqslant v_1 > 0 \tag{3.9}$$

the Cauchy's initial value problem of dynamic viscoelasticity has at most one solution in $P \cup V(T)$.

REFERENCES

1. I. Herrera R. and M. E. Gurtin, *Quart. Appl. Math.* **22**, 360–364 (1965).
2. B. D. Coleman, M. E. Gurtin, and I. Herrera R. Waves in materials with memory, I, *Arch. Rational Mech. Anal.* **19**, 239–265 (1965).
3. B. D. Coleman and M. E. Gurtin, Waves in materials with memory II, III, IV, *Arch. Rational Mech. Anal.* (1965).
4. B. D. Coleman and M. E. Gurtin, Thermodynamics and wave propagation, Tech. Rept. 100, Div. Appl. Math., Brown Univ., Providence, Rhode Island (1965).

5. E. Varley, Acceleration fronts in viscoelastic materials, *Arch. Rational Mech. Anal.* **19**, 215–225 (1965).

6. R. D. Glanx and E. H. Lee, *J. Appl. Phys.* **25**, 947–953 (1954).

7. E. H. Lee and I. Kanter, *J. Appl. Phys.* **24**, 1115 (1953).

8. V. Volterra, Sulle equazione integro-differenziali della teoria dell' elasticita. *Atti Reale Accad. Lincei* **18**, 2, 195 (1909).

9. E. T. Onat and S. Brever, On uniqueness in linear viscoelasticity, *in* "Progress in Applied Mechanics, Prager Anniversary Volume." Macmillan, New York, 1963.

10. M. E. Gurtin and E. Sternberg, On the linear theory of viscoelasticity, *Arch. Rational Mech. Anal.* **11**, 4, 291 (1962).

11. W. S. Eldestein and M. E. Gurtin, Uniqueness theorems in the linear dynamic theory of anisotropic viscoelastic solids, *Arch. Rational Mech. Anal.* **17**, 47–60 (1964).

12. F. Odeh and I. Tadjbakhsch, Uniqueness in the linear theory of viscoelasticity, *Arch. Rational Mech. Anal.* **18**, 244–250 (1965).

13. R. Courant and D. Hilbert, "Methods of Mathematical Physics," Vol. II. Wiley (Interscience), New York, 1962.

On an Isothermal Flow Function for a Heterogeneous Medium

D. R. AXELRAD

Department of Mechanical Engineering
McGill University
Montreal, Canada

R. N. YONG

Department of Civil Engineering and Applied Mechanics and Soil Mechanics
McGill University
Montreal, Canada

1. Introduction

A heterogeneous medium consisting of an arbitrary number of phases may be termed a "multi-phase system." Such media usually possess a random phase geometry. A special type of such media is a "two-phase system" where one phase is considered as the matrix in which the other phase is embedded in form of a dispersion of particles of special shape and dimensions. The physical constants of such media are random functions of space. Most of the investigation to date are based on a continuum mechanistic approach with the necessary restrictions of this theory. An actual field analysis of heterogeneous media has not been developed as yet. Some special results however of such a theory are available. In this connection some recent investigations in the field of elastic multi-phase media consisting of isotropic phases are mentioned in Kröner,[1] Hill,[2] Paul,[3] and Budiansky *et al.*[4]

The present investigation is concerned with the formulation of a flow function (isothermal) of a heterogeneous medium such as an organic clay, which is of considerable interest in soil mechanics. The inorganic clay typifying an inhomogeneous medium possesses a microstructure of "super molecular" dimensions and where the individual inhomogeneities representing the structure are either geometrical or physical parameters of a random nature. Thus in general the mechanical behavior of such a system when subjected to a constant input of stress will be represented by a stress state the characteristic quantities of which are random functions of space and time. In this paper an attempt is made to formulate a flow function for the heterogeneous medium under the test conditions described subsequently and to correlate this function with the experimentally obtained data.

2.   Physical Constants and Microstress-Strain Relations

The random arrangement of the phases of an inorganic clay (degenerate kaolinite) is shown in Fig. 1 which represents a three-dimensional view of a cross section. The random geometry of the phases in a typical transverse cross section of a cylindrical specimen of the material is indicated in Fig. 2. It is evident that in order to relate macroscopic

FIG. 1   Three-dimensional schematic of actual clay network.

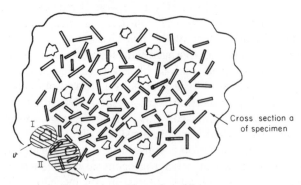

FIG. 2   Assemblage of particles.

observable quantities to microscopic inhomogeneities of the medium, the linear dimensions of a small region (R) in which micro stresses and strains occur, must be defined. The smallest linear dimensions (in all directions) of a physical point of the medium, where the characteristic properties in a continuum mechanistic sense are still retained would be for this material of the order of $\sim 10^4$ Å. Hence, considering a typical point "I" with volume v, where the microstresses ζ_{ij} act and another point "II" with volume V, at which the actual macroscopic stress components σ_{ij} are applied (Fig. 2), then the physical constants may be defined by

$$
\begin{aligned}
a_{ij}^{(M)} &= \lim_{R \to V} a_{ij}^{(R)} & b_{ij}^{(M)} &= \lim_{R \to V} b_{ij}^{(R)} \\
a_{ij}^{(m)} &= \lim_{R \to v} a_{ij}^{(R)} & b_{ij}^{(m)} &= \lim_{R \to v} b_{ij}^{(R)}
\end{aligned}
\tag{1}
$$

where the superscripts refer to macroscopic and microscopic quantities a_{ij}, b_{ij} and where a representative volume Ω of the medium is of a magnitude such that $\Omega \gg V \gg v$.[5] Denoting by $a^{(\kappa)}$ the small cross sectional areas of mutually nonintersecting sections of volume v within the region of point II and assuming equilibrium to exist, then the normal components of the macroscopic stress tensor in terms of the microscopic ones can be written as

$$
\sigma_{ij} = \sum_{(\kappa)} \zeta_{ij}^{(\kappa)} \frac{a^{(\kappa)}}{A}
\tag{2}
$$

in which A denotes the total cross sectional area of the specimen. Hence, the macro- and microstress-deformation relations within the elastic region may be expressed as follows:

$$
\begin{aligned}
e_{ij} &= \sum_{(\kappa)} a_{ij}^{(M)} \sigma_{j\kappa} & \sigma_{ij} &= \sum_{(\kappa)} b_{ij}^{(M)} e_{j\kappa} \\
\varepsilon_{ij} &= \sum_{(\kappa)} a_{ij}^{(m)} \zeta_{j\kappa} & \zeta_{ij} &= \sum_{(\kappa)} b_{ij}^{(m)} \varepsilon_{j\kappa}
\end{aligned}
\tag{3}
$$

in which ε_{ij}, e_{ij} denote the components of the micro- and macroscopic small strain tensor, respectively. Assuming the existence of a large number of areas $a^{(\kappa)}$ in section A, then the components of the microstress tensor can be expressed by the mathematical expectation or the first moment of the distribution function of the random variable ζ_{ij}, and similarly for the other quantities. However for a complete statistical description of the physical constants as well as the microstresses and microstrains, the knowledge of all their probability distributions (second moments, etc.) with respect to any (κ) point system in space for any configuration would be required. By using the ergodic hypothesis of statistical theory, the ensemble average of the relevant quantities can be replaced by the volume average over a sufficiently large region of the specimen. Hence, assuming that the averages and correlation functions of the physical quantities for the material under consideration can be determined, the corresponding macroscopic stress-deformation relations may then be expressed by[6]

$$\bar{e}_{ij} = P_1 \bar{\sigma}_{ij} \qquad \bar{\sigma}_{ij} = P_2 \bar{e}_{ij} \tag{4}$$

where the overbar indicates the ensemble averages of the relevant quantities and the operators P_1, P_2 depending on the type of heterogeneous media, may be constants, differential or integral time operators.

3. Formulation of the Flow Function of a Heterogeneous Medium

The isothermal mechanical response of two-phase media to a constant input of stress has been investigated in Axelrad.[7,8] The microstructural conditions of such dispersed media were accounted for by introducing a "stiffness parameter" and an isothermal "structure function." The former was defined as the ratio of the incremental (macroscopic) stress deviator to the strain deviator. It was further assumed that the macroscopic deviatoric components of stress and strain are linearly related in the flow region so that the stiffness parameter becomes

$$\phi_s = \frac{\partial \bar{\sigma}'_{ij}}{\partial \bar{e}'_{ij}} \tag{5}$$

and

$$\bar{\sigma}'_{ij} = \bar{\sigma}_{ij} - \tfrac{1}{3}\bar{\sigma}_{ii}\,\delta_{ij} \qquad \bar{e}'_{ij} = \bar{e}_{ij} - \tfrac{1}{3}\bar{e}_{ii}\,\delta_{ij} \tag{6}$$

where the previously introduced notation for ensemble averages has been used and δ_{ij} is the Kronecker symbol (i.e., $\delta_{ij} = 0$, $i \neq j$, $\delta_{ij} = 1$, $i = j$). In deriving the phenomenological strain-time or flow function for such materials, it has been assumed that at each representative volume element, the deviatoric stress components can be related to the microstructure of the systems, which in the adopted notation becomes

$$\bar{\sigma}'_{ij} = \psi_s\{\langle e \rangle, \langle D \rangle, \langle d \rangle, \ldots, \bar{e}'_{ij}, t\} \tag{7}$$

in which ψ_s is a function of the geometrical parameters, i.e., $\langle e \rangle$ the average volume or weight ratio of the two phases, $\langle D \rangle$ the mean particle size of the dispersed phase, $\langle d \rangle$ the mean spacing, etc., and also a function of $\bar{e}'_{ij}$ and time. To simplify the analysis, however, an approximation of ψ_s will be used, since the most significant parameter in the study of an inorganic clay is the volume fraction $\langle e \rangle$, which itself is dependent on $\bar{e}'_{ij}$. Hence, relation (7) may be written as

$$\bar{\sigma}'_{ij} \cong \psi_s[\bar{e}'_{ij}, t] \tag{8}$$

From the point of view of irreversible thermodynamics by taking volume densities of the internal energy, the free energy, entropy of a specimen element (surrounding point II), the components of the stress and strain tensor, the heat received by the element in time dt, then the inner energy density can be expressed by

$$du = dq + \bar{\sigma}'_{ij}\, d\bar{e}'_{ij} \qquad T\, ds = dq + T\zeta \tag{9}$$

Combining these relations gives:

$$-T\zeta\, dt = du - T\, ds - \bar{\sigma}'_{ij}\, d\bar{e}'_{ij} = df - \bar{\sigma}'_{ij}\, d\bar{e}'_{ij} \tag{10}$$

where ζ denotes the entropy production rate and f the free energy density of the 2-phase system. The latter is considered as a "closed" system within the representative volume, although each phase within this volume is an "open" system in itself, since it may exchange matter with the other phase. It has been shown by Prigogine[9] for instance on basis of statistical mechanics that Eq. (10) remains valid for any differential changes (reversible or irreversible) from the equilibrium state. On this basis an equation of state of the following form can be assumed:

$$f = f\{s, \zeta_2, \zeta_3, \ldots, \zeta_n\} \tag{11}$$

where the entropy $s \equiv \zeta_1$, and the other state variables ζ are counted from $i = 2, 3, \ldots, n$. In terms of these variables, which may contain other parameters to account for physicochemical interactions, electrostatic effects, etc., between the phases and the "generalized" forces X_i, the relation (10) may be expressed as follows:

$$T\, ds^{(i)} = df - X_i^{(i)}\, d\zeta_i \tag{12}$$

where the superscript (i) refers to the irreversible parts of the entropy and generalized forces, respectively. Thus,

$$X_i = X_i^{(r)} + X_i^{(i)} \tag{13a}$$

$$X_i^{(r)} = \left[\frac{\partial f}{\partial \zeta_i}\right]_{s=\text{const.}} \qquad X_i^{(i)} = T\left[\frac{\partial s^{(i)}}{\partial \zeta_i}\right]_{V=\text{const.}} = b_{ij}\dot{\zeta}_j \tag{13b}$$

In relation (13b) Onsager's theorem has been used, i.e., that the forces are linear functions of the fluxes $\dot{\zeta}_j$ and the phenomenological coefficients are symmetric tensors ($b_{ij} = b_{ji} \geqslant 0$, b_{ij}^{-1} being the inverse matrix of b_{ij}). By expanding the free energy density in form of a power series and using a two term approximation, the generalized forces have then the form

$$X_i = X_i^{(i)} + a_{ij}\dot{\zeta}_j = a_{ij}\zeta_j + b_{ij}\dot{\zeta}_j \tag{14}$$

It should be noted that the coefficients a_{ij} are also symmetric, i.e., that $a_{ij} = a_{ji}$ and that the condition $a_{ij} \geqslant 0, b_{ij} \geqslant 0$ mean that the quadratic form with the numerical factors a_{ij}, b_{ij} are both positive and definite.

The solution of Eq. (14) leads to the strain-time function of a two-phase medium,[8] which in terms of the average quantities may be written as

$$\bar{e}'_{ij}(t) = a_{ij}\bar{\sigma}'_{ij}(t) + b_{ij}^{-1}\int_0^t \exp[-b_{ij}^{-1}a_{ij}(t-\tau)]\bar{\sigma}'_{ij}(\tau)\,d\tau \qquad (15)$$

4. Experimental Considerations

For the experimental part of the study accelerated creep tests on an inorganic clay (degenerate kaolinite) were carried out. The test arrangement is shown schematically in Fig. 3. The load was applied monotonically to a cylindrical specimen of the material, which was initially in equilibrium and under isotropic stress condition. Variations of the initial isotropic stress produced corresponding variations in the initial equilibrium volume or weight fraction of the specimen. A typical dispersion of solid clay particles in the liquid-solid system has already been indicated in Fig. 2. The experimental observations of the macroscopic strain under the above test conditions revealed a linear relationship between the macroscopic deviatoric stress and strain components at various time levels in the flow regions, thus confirming the assumption of the stiffness parameter ϕ_s in Eq. (5). The plot of the observed strains against the observed stress σ_{11} is shown in Fig. 4. A strain-time relationship at various stress levels σ_{11} resulted in typical flow curves shown in Fig. 5. For the purpose of comparing the formulated flow function for the heterogeneous medium as given in Eq. (15) with the experimentally obtained flow curves, curve (1) of Fig. 5 was replotted together with the

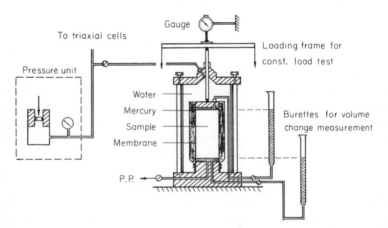

FIG. 3   Schematic of experimental test.

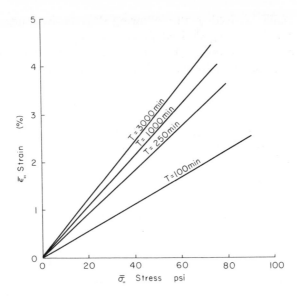

FIG. 4   Observed stress-strain relationship in the flow region.

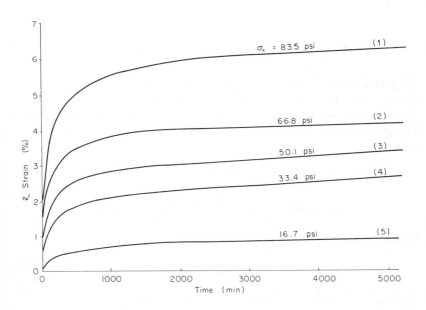

FIG. 5   Typical flow curves at various stress levels.

calculated values derived in the following (Fig. 6). Recalling that the symmetric tensors a_{ij}, b_{ij} derived in Section 3 from thermodynamic considerations by expressing the free energy density and dissipation function, (corresponding to the $X_i^{(i)}, s$) the bracket expression of the

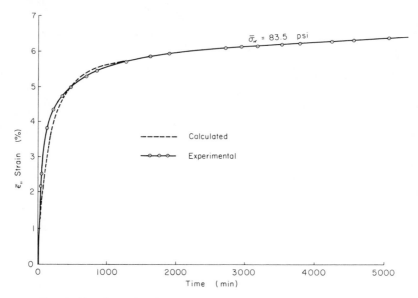

FIG. 6   Experimental and calculated curves for a representative stress level.

integrand in Eq. (15) may be considered as a "thermodynamic impedance" function (see also Axelrad[10]). Hence, for the given test conditions were the macroscopic stress σ_{11} is considered as constant and by neglecting the initial elastic response for $t \to 0$, relation (15) can be written as follows:

$$\bar{e}'_{ij}(t) = b_{ij}^{-1} \exp[-b_{ij}^{-1}a_{ij} \cdot t] \int_0^t \exp[b_{ij}^{-1}a_{ij} \cdot \tau] \cdot \bar{\sigma}'_{ij}(\tau)\, d\tau$$

$$= b_{ij}^{-1} \exp[-b_{ij}^{-1}a_{ij} \cdot t]^0 \left[\frac{1}{b_{ij}^{-1}a_{ij}}\right] \exp[b_{ij}^{-1}a_{ij}\tau]\Big|_0^t \cdot \bar{\sigma}^i_{ij}(t) \qquad (16)$$

Hence

$$\bar{e}'_{ij}(t) = \frac{\bar{\sigma}'_{ij}(t)}{a_{ij}} \left[1 - \exp[-b_{ij}^{-1}a_{ij} \cdot t]\right] \qquad (17)$$

Let $a_{ij}^{-1} = A$, $a_{ij}b_{ij}^{-1} = B$; then for the test conditions

$$\bar{e}_{11} = A\{1 - e^{-Bt}\}\bar{\sigma}_{11} \qquad (18)$$

Assuming that the individual responses of (k) ensemble elements within the region of the representative volume (V) are linear functions of the individual inputs a more general relation corresponding to Eq. (18) may be written as follows:

$$\bar{e}_{11}(t) = \left[\sum_{\kappa=1}^{\infty} a_\kappa [1 - \exp[-b_\kappa t]] \right] \overline{\sigma_{11}}(t) \tag{19}$$

where the bracket expression represents the slope to the flow curve at any time t. Take a 3-element approximation and evaluate the corresponding constants; this yields

$$e_{11} \doteq 2.39 \times 10^{-4} \{ [1 - e^{-0.01t}] + [1 - e^{-0.003t}] + [1 - e^{-0.0015t}] \} \sigma_{11}$$

$$\tag{20}$$

a comparison of the curve obtained from a plot of Eq. (20) shows close agreement with the experimentally obtained curve.

ACKNOWLEDGMENT

The authors wish to acknowledge the experimental work performed by D. S. Chen under contract arrangement between the Defense Research Board of Canada and R. N. Yong, and K. M. Jassby, of the Department of Mechanical Engineering, McGill University, Montreal, Canada, for assistance in the preparation of the manuscript.

REFERENCES

1. E. Kröner, Berechnung der elastischen Konstanten der Vielkristalle aus den Konstanten der Einkristalle, *Z. Physik.* **151**, 504 (1958).
2. R. Hill, Report on theories of the elastic properties of reinforced solids, *Mech. Phys. Solids* **11**, 357 (1963).
3. B. Paul, Prediction of elastic constants of multiphase materials, *Trans. AIME* **218**, 36 (1960).
4. B. Budiansky, Z. Hashin, and T. L. Sanders, The stressfield of a slipped crystal and the early plastic behavior of polycrystalline materials, *Proc. 2nd Symp. Naval Structural Mech.* Pergamon Press, Oxford, 1960.
5. L. D. Landau and E. M. Lifschitz, "Theory of Elasticity." Addison-Wesley, Reading, Massachusetts, 1959.
6. Z. Hashin, Theory of mechanical behavior of heterogeneous media, *Appl. Mech. Rev.* **17**, no. 1 (1964).
7. D. R. Axelrad, On the deformation of 2-phase systems at high temperature, *J. Soc. Mat. Sci. Japan* **12**, 322 (1963).
8. D. R. Axelrad, On the thermo-rheology of a 2-phase systems, *J. Soc. Mat. Sci. Japan* **14**, 139 (1965).
9. I. Prigogine, "Introduction to Thermodynamics of Irreversible Processes," 2nd ed. Wiley, New York, 1961.
10. D. R. Axelrad, The rheological stress-strain relation in solids, *T.A.M. Rept. No.* 213 (1963), Dept. Theor. Appl. Mech., Univ. Illinois, Urbana, Illinois.

Mass Transfer into Non-Newtonian Fluids

VAUGHN C. BEHN and GERALD A. STROBEL†

School of Civil Engineering
Cornell University
Ithaca, New York

1. Introduction

The work described in this report is concerned with a study of diffusion of benzoic acid at constant temperature into kaolinite slurries of varying concentration.[1] Diffusivities were obtained by recirculating the non-Newtonian slurry under laminar flow conditions through a soluble cast tube of benzoic acid. The diffusivity of benzoic acid was then calculated utilizing the assumption that under laminar flow conditions the mass of benzoic acid will penetrate only a small distance into the slurry.[2] The values of diffusivity of benzoic acid into suspensions of 10, 15, 20, and 25% by weight kaolinite could then be compared with that into water at the same temperature (approximately 20°C). The formula to be used in comparing the diffusion into a non-Newtonian suspension with that of water was presented by Clough *et al.*[3] This formula is in effect an extension of Eyring's rate theory of mass transfer.

2. Theory

The basic differential equation for material diffusing into a flowing liquid in a cylinder is

$$\frac{u\,\partial c}{\partial z} = D\left[\frac{\partial^2 c}{\partial r^2} + \frac{1}{r}\frac{\partial c}{\partial r}\right] \tag{1}$$

where

u = local fluid velocity LT^{-1}
z = longitudinal coordinate of mass transfer system, L
c = concentration, ML^{-3}.

r = radius coordinate of mass transfer system, L
D = diffusivity, L^2T^{-1}

† *Present address:* Shellfisheries Management Unit, State of New York Conservation Department, Oakdale, Long Island, New York.

In the case involving heat transfer, Leveque made the assumption that the value for the local velocity, u, could be substituted for by a constant, α, times the distance y traveled in diffusing:

$$u = \alpha y \qquad (2)$$

where $y = r_w - r$, r_w being the actual radius of the pipe in which diffusion was taking place.

For a non-Newtonian fluid α is the shear rate at the wall:

$$\alpha = \frac{8V}{d} \frac{(3n' + 1)}{4n'} \qquad (3)$$

where V = mean velocity of flow, LT^{-1}.
d = diameter of capillary, L.
n' = flow behavior index for fluids of unspecified shear rate–shear stress relationship, dimensionless.

Combining these equations with the Whitman model for K_L, the liquid film coefficient, results in Eq. (4) for calculating diffusivity of benzoic acid into the kaolinite suspension[2]:

$$D_{nn} = \frac{1}{L}\left(\frac{\rho}{w\delta}\right)^{1/2}\left(\frac{V_f}{5.5t_r}\right)^{3/2}\left(\ln\frac{C_s - C_i}{C_s - C_f}\right)^{3/2} \qquad (4)$$

where
D_{nn} = diffusivity into a non-Newtonian fluid, $L^{-2}1^{-1}$.
L = tube length, L.
ρ = fluid density, ML^{-3}.
w = fluid mass rate, MT^{-1}.
V_f = fluid volume, L^3.
t_r = time of diffusion run, T.

C_s, C_i, C_f = saturation, initial, and final values of concentration, ML^{-3}.

$$\delta = \frac{\alpha}{8V/d} = \frac{3n' + 1}{4n'},$$

dimensionless.
n' = flow behavior index, dimensionless.

The diffusivities calculated by Eq. (4) were then compared with an equation presented by Clough et al. which is an extension of Eyring's rate theory of mass transfer.[3] Clough et al. have written the following equation for diffusion into a non-Newtonian fluid, where the fluid contains inert suspended solids:

$$D_{nn} = \sum_{n=1}^{v} \chi_n D_n = \chi_{cp} D_{cp} \qquad (5)$$

where χ is the volume fraction occupied by each particular phase of the non-Newtonian fluid, and the subscript cp refers to the continuous phase of the suspension not occupied by any suspended particles.

Now Ree and Eyring had previously offered the following expression for diffusion into a Newtonian solution[4]:

$$D = \frac{kTk'}{\lambda \xi k'' \mu} \cdot \frac{d \ln a}{d \ln c} \tag{6}$$

where

D = diffusivity into Newtonian fluid.

T = absolute temperature.

k = Boltzmann's constant.

$k'k''$ = frequency factors in the solution and pure liquid

μ = viscosity.

λ = distance of two equilibrium positions for flow in direction of shear.

a = activity.

c = concentration.

ξ = number of viscous shears of neighboring molecules whose movement is opposite to that of diffusing molecule.

The ratio of D_{nn} to D can be found by using Eqs. (5) and (6), assuming that the ratio of the several variables (except for those given in Eq. (7)) would be approximately one[3]:

$$\frac{D_{nn}}{D} = \chi_{cp} \frac{\xi}{\xi_{cp}} \frac{\mu}{\mu_{cp}} \tag{7}$$

In Eq. (7) the subscript cp refers to the continuous phase. The ratio ξ/ξ_{cp} represents the number of viscous shears in water to that in the continuous phase. μ/μ_{cp} represents the ratio of viscosities reached at very high shear rates. χ_{cp} is the fractional volume of the continuous phase. As such χ_{cp} is difficult to calculate with precision because the actual amount of hydration of the suspension is unknown. Nevertheless, a figure can be assigned to it with some reliance. This means that the quantity ξ/ξ_{cp} is the remaining unknown in Eq. (7). When values of this ratio are calculated Eq. (7), if correct, can be used to solve for diffusivities into non-Newtonians.

3. Experimental Apparatus

As shown in Fig. 1, the experimental model used was a system where the kaolinite slurry was recirculated in laminar motion at a constant 20°C through a soluble cast tube of benzoic acid. The inside diameter

Vaughn C. Behn and Gerald A. Strobel

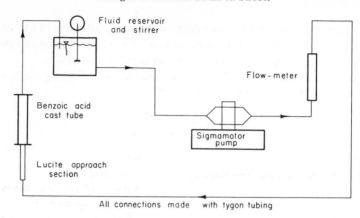

FIG. 1   Flow diagram for mass transfer system.

of the benzoic acid tube was $\frac{1}{2}$ in. and the length was 18 in. After the tube the mixture went to a 5 liter fluid reservoir with stirrer. The material was pumped by a Sigmamotor pump no. T65 through a flow-meter to the benzoic acid tube.

Prior to each run, the rheological properties of the kaolinite suspensions had to be established. The value of n' for each per cent by weight of kaolinite was found using the experimental arrangement shown in Fig. 2.[5]

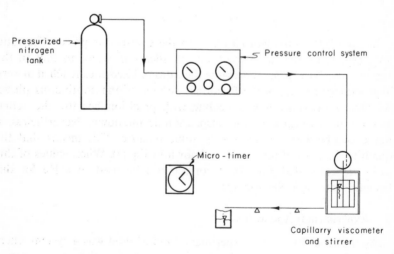

FIG. 2   Flow diagram for viscometric system.

Details of the experimental equipment used are available.[1,2] All of the test runs were conducted in a constant temperature room at approximately 20°C.

4. Experimental Procedure

The slurry samples were prepared by drying a sample of kaolinite at 103°C. The sample was then weighed and added to a predetermined weight of distilled water. The suspensions used in this study were 10, 15, 20, and 25% kaolinite by weight. It should be noted here that a 5% solution was prepared, but it was found to become turbulent at relatively low rates of shear and was not used.

The kaolinite suspensions were then tested in the capillary viscometer and found to be slightly thixotropic. That is to say some variation of n' occurred with varying capillary tube. Nevertheless, it was felt that results within experimental error could be obtained with a 0.216 cm diameter by 153.1 cm length tube. We followed the procedure of Read[2] in allowing at least one hour of recirculation before running the test to calculate n'.

The saturation of benzoic acid into kaolinite suspension was found by allowing the suspension to circulate through the diffusion system until three successive kaolinite samples showed no change in benzoic acid concentration. The amount of benzoic acid was determined by titration with base to an electrometic end point.

The mass transfer tests, involving the set of data in Eq. (4), were run on each of the four benzoic acid concentrations. Further details are given in the thesis by Strobel.[1]

5. Experimental Results

The suspension flow parameters are given in Table I, the saturation concentration of benzoic acid in kaolinite to suspension in Table II, and the diffusion parameters are given in Table III. In comparing D_{nn}

TABLE I
SLURRY FLOW PARAMETERS

Concentration (%) (kaolinite by wt.)	n'	Density (gm/cc)
10	0.802	1.065
15	0.663	1.105
20	0.574	1.141
25	0.306	1.187

TABLE II
SATURATION CONCENTRATION OF BENZOIC ACID IN KAOLINITE SLURRY

Concentration (%) (kaolinite by wt.)	Temperature (°C)	Saturation concentration benzoic acid (gm/liter)
10	20.5	2.510
	21.0	2.460
15	20.0	2.543
	21.5	2.558
20	20.0	2.506
	22.0	2.543
25	21.0	2.485
	21.5	2.516

TABLE III
DIFFUSION PARAMETERS FOR KAOLINITE SLURRIES

Concentration (%) (kaolinite by wt.)	$D_{nn} \times 10^5$ (cm^2/sec)	X_{cp} (%)	μ_{cp} (poises)	ξ/ξ_{cp}
10	3.05	91.8	0.0120	3.98
15	3.40	90.4	0.0140	5.86
20	3.52	89.3	0.0198	8.73
25	3.77	86.4	0.0220	9.21

given in Table III with D, the diffusion of benzoic acid into water a value of $D = 0.9 \times 10^{-5}$ cm^2 sec^{-1} was used.[1] Also the viscosity of water was taken as $\mu = 0.01$ poise. To find μ_{cp} we took the viscosity of the suspension of an inverse of shear rate equal to zero.[3]

6. Discussion

First as regards Table I, it is apparent that we obtained a truly wide range of non-Newtonian behavior with the value of n' equal to 0.802 at 10% kaolinite suspension to $n' = 0.306$ at 25% concentration. From Table II we conclude that the concentration of kaolinite does not influence the saturation concentration of benzoic acid. Generally speaking there is a dimunition in concentration as one goes from 15 to 25% kaolinite. In other words we can support Read's findings that there was no adsorption taking place.[2]

This leaves us with Table III or Fig. 3. Table III says that instead of decreasing with increasing slurry concentration the actual value of D_{nn} was found to increase. In other words for kaolinite concentrations of 10 to 25% by weight, D_{nn} varied from 3.05 to 3.77 × 10^{-5} cm^2/sec.

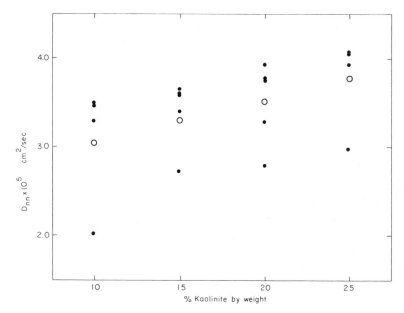

FIG. 3 Diffusivity vs concentration.

If we take up consideration of the ratio ξ/ξ_{cp} we see that the calculated value ranges from 3.98 to 9.21 with an increase in concentration of from 10 to 25%. If ξ for pure water is taken as 15,[3] then ξ_{cp} must decrease from 3.98 to 1.6 for the increase from 10 to 25% in kaolinite. Perhaps then we can assume that the diffusing species is mainly associated with the suspending particles. But there is no evidence for this association, and in fact there is the evidence above cited with respect to solubilities that there is no association.

We conclude from this that Eq. (7) is not sufficient to explain the results obtained. The findings of an increased diffusivity could be explained by either turbulent flow or adsorbtion of the benzoic acid molecule on the clay, but we do not believe that either of these factors were present. A factor involving the motion of the clay particles might serve to answer the problem, but our results, as well as previously reported data,[3] do not indicate that the diffusion is a function of the shear rate. Astarita has reported in some diffusion data involving a gas taken up by a non-Newtonian liquid.[6] He notes that similar to our data he gets D_{nn} values which are higher than D. Metzner has tentatively suggested that the suspension may in fact be structured in such a manner as to permit regions of high diffusivity in the immediate vicinity of the added particles.[7] In any case the basic notion that diffusion rates increase with the presence of suspended material is an extremely interesting one.

7. Summary and Conclusions

This report considers diffusivity of benzoic acid into kaolinite slurries of varying concentration. The interesting aspect of the experimental work is the ratio of diffusion into kaolinite suspension, D_{nn}, to that into water, D, varied from 3.05 to $3.77 \times 10^{-5} \text{ cm}^2/\text{sec}$ as the kaolinite concentration increased from 10 to 25%. The values were then used to calculate ξ/ξ_{cp} which fell off much too rapidly. This would assume that the diffusing species is mainly associated with the suspending particle, but since there was also a decrease in saturation concentration with increasing kaolinite concentration we do not believe there was any assimilation of the benzoic acid by the clay. We are still seeking means to explain this data.

ACKNOWLEDGMENT

The authors gratefully acknowledge that this work was supported by a Public Health Service Grant, WP-229, from the Division of Water Supply and Pollution Control.

REFERENCES

1. G. A. Strobel, A study of diffusivity into non-Newtonian slurries, M.S. Thesis, Cornell University, Ithaca, New York (1965).
2. H. E. Read, The effect of shear rate upon diffusion coefficients for non-Newtonian fluids, M.M.E. Thesis, University of Delaware, Newark, Delaware (1961).
3. S. B. Clough, H. E. Read, A. B. Metzner, and V. C. Behn, Diffusion in slurries and in non-Newtonian fluids, *A.I.Ch.E.J.* **8**, 346 (1962).
4. T. Ree and H. Eyring, The relaxation theory of transport phenomena, *in* "Rheology" (F. R. Eirich, ed.), Vol. 2, Chapt. 3, p. 98. Academic Press, New York, 1958.
5. V. C. Behn, Experimental determination of sludge-flow parameters, *J. Sanit. Eng. Div, Proc. Am. Soc. Civil Engrs.* **88**, SA3, 39 (1962).
6. G. Astarita, Communication, diffusivity in non-Newtonian liquids, *Ind. Eng. Chem. Fundamentals* **4**, 236 (1965).
7. A. B. Metzner, Diffusive transport rates in structured media. Unpublished manuscript, Dept. Chem. Eng., Univ. Delaware, Newark, Delaware (1965).

INDEX

Acceleration
  compressive, 168
  expansive, 168
  wave, 165
Aggregate, 13, 14
  deformation, 14
Alumina, 19, 20

Beam theory, 66
Benzoic acid, 193
Birefringence, optical, 19, 20
Buffer zone, 152
Burgers vector, 69, 70

Caloric equation, 6, 12
Cauchy–Green tensor, 111, 118, 133
Clausius–Duhem inequality, 5
Clausius–Planck inequality, 3
Compatibility, 109
Constitutive equation, 53, 89, 125
  incompressible second order fluid, 73
  perfect incompressible, 91
  perfect compressible, 91
  simple material, 129
  viscous incompressible, 91
Cosserat
  continua, 66
  theory, 65
Couette flow, 73, 129

Decomposition, polar, 67
Deformation
  aggregate, 14
  elastic, 89
  frequency, 153
  gradient, 67, 134, 165
  history, 134
  rapid, 11
  relative, 135
  shearing, 19
  temperature history, 7, 8, 11, 12
  tensor, 67

Diffusion, rotary, 28
Diffusivity, 114, 199
Dipolar medium, 69, 70
Dislocation
  Cosserat theory, 65
  density, 69
  strain, 70
Displacement
  gradient, 93
  matrix, 15
  tensor, 13, 14
Dissipation
  energy, 51
  inequality, 6, 7, 9
  wave number, 37, 51, 52
Drag reduction, 37, 38

Einstein tensor, 113
Elasticity
  finite, 109
  nonlinear theory, 54, 91
  tensor, 176
Ellipsoidal particles, 27
Energy
  balance, 3, 67, 68
  efflux, 4
  flux, 11
  storage, 16
  supply, 4
Equation of state, 3
Equipresence principle, 8

Flow
  function, 186
  slurry, 197
  viscometric, 129
Free energy, 10–12
Frequency
  of tumbling, 153
  parameter, 77

Galerkin method, 73

Inorganic clay, 188
Internal dissipation, 5, 9, 10
Irreversibility, 5, 11
Isotropic elastic solid, 12

Kirchhoff's method, 139

Law of the wall, 151

Macromolecule
  coil, 153
  gyration, 37
Mass
  random close-packed, 13
  transfer, 193
Material
  coefficient, 68
  isotropic, 125
  frame indifference, 134
  simple, 8, 129, 130
  short memory, 74
  with fading memory, 7, 8, 11, 12, 74, 94
  with long range memory, 11, 92
  with memory, 11
  with no memory, 11
  with stored energy function, 12
Medium, heterogeneous, 183, 186
Memory, fading, 170, 172
Microstress
  deformation, 185
  strain relations, 184
Molecular, entanglement, 156
Molecular processes, 14
Molecular viscoelasticity, 145
Momentum balance, 166
Motion
  invariant, 135, 136
  short, 97
  small, 96
Multiphase system, 183
Multipolar, 68

Navier–Stokes equation, 6, 90
Nonpolar, 68

Polymer, 19, 37, 147
  concentration, 42
Poiseuille flow, 129, 160
Propagation
  equation, 21
  shear wave, 19

Quasi-elastic response, 8, 10, 11
Quasi-static process, 2

Refraction index, 22
Relaxation tensor, 177, 181
Reversible process, 2, 11
Rheoelectric analogy, 140
Rici identities, 113
Riemann tensor, 113
Rivlin–Ericksen
  coefficient, 104
  fluid, 130, 131
  materials, 8
  tensor, 73, 130, 131
Rotation
  gradient, 67
  tensor, 15

Second order fluid, 73, 74
Shear
  critical, 48
  gradient, 20
  history, 94, 103
  layer, 159
  plane, 21
  rate, 14, 92
  real, 62, 63
  stress, 37, 146
  wave, 19, 20, 22, 25, 32
  wavelength, 20
Shearing
  deformation, 19
  motion, 92
Shearing motion
  unsteady, 90, 104
Simple fluid, 73, 129
Simple material with memory, 169

Solutions
  diagonal, 57
  nondiagonal, 57, 58
Stability
  laminar flow, 74
  of flow, 73
  onset, 74
Stokes–Duhem inequality, 7
Strain
  deformation equation, 125
  history, 170
  invariant, 110, 117
  matrix, 15
  principal, 110
Stiffness parameter, 188
Stress
  relaxation function, 94
  threshold, 147
Stretching tensor, 6
Sublayer, 152

Taylor number, 73
Thermodynamics, 2, 12
  of deformation, 7
Thermostatics, 2, 12
Thin jet theory, 143
Time
  relaxation, 28, 29
  stress-relaxation, 96
Toms phenomenon, 37, 145

Turbulent
  energy, 51
  pipe flow, 146
  production, 51
  scale, 50
  shear flow, 38

Viscoelastic
  constitutive relation, 168
  flow, 89, 91, 94
  linear, 179
  material, 74, 175
  properties, 20
Viscosity
  coefficient, 21
  complex, 21, 28
  flow, 28, 29
  intrinsic, 48
  solvent, 29, 31, 33
  zero-shear, 153

Wave
  acceleration, 165
  diffraction, 26
  in elastic materials, 167
  length, 21, 23, 166
  number, 83
  shear, 19, 20, 22, 25, 32
  velocity, 21
Wavelength of disturbance, 76